Chemical
Anthropology

Chemical Anthropology

*A New Approach
to Growth in Children*

By Icie G. Macy *and* Harriet J. Kelly

 THE UNIVERSITY OF CHICAGO PRESS

Library of Congress Catalog Number: 57-11931

THE UNIVERSITY OF CHICAGO PRESS, CHICAGO 37
Cambridge University Press, London, N.W. 1, England
The University of Toronto Press, Toronto 5, Canada

© 1957 by The University of Chicago
Published 1957. Composed and printed by
THE UNIVERSITY OF CHICAGO PRESS
Chicago, Illinois, U.S.A.

To the revered memory and contributions of the late Hugo A. Freund, M.D., president of the Board of Trustees, Children's Fund of Michigan, whose wisdom, sound judgment, scientific research interests, and personal encouragement inspired confidence and effort on the part of the staff beyond the call of duty, and who envisioned the results of these studies as

a mosaic for those who would visualize the early chemical processes of life and the progressive changes expressed in terms of the actual metabolic activities of the normal child. It need not be emphasized that a knowledge of biochemical and metabolic processes is essential before an understanding of deviations from the normal, and pathologic changes, can be properly evaluated by the practitioner of medicine.

—Foreword by Dr. Freund
Nutrition and Chemical Growth in Childhood

Preface

This is one of a series of interpretative publications on the studies of the fundamental aspects of chemical growth and nutrition of children carried out under the sponsorship of the Children's Fund of Michigan and the Merrill-Palmer School. The experimental details, original data, and statistical information are recorded in the three volumes of *Nutrition and Chemical Growth in Childhood*, which serve as the basis for the analyses and discussions presented here. The first volume of that series contains an extensive bibliography which the reader may find of value. Therefore in this publication only essential and new references are included.

This volume briefly summarizes the results of specific phases of our research and presents them in general terms of childhood; future publications will present specific detailed considerations of variabilities in growth observed in the individual child as he grows, develops, and adapts physiologically.

The research leading to this publication resulted from an interest initiated and long stimulated by the authors' association in the fields of nutrition, growth, and development of children. The senior author assumed responsibility for the nutrition and chemical phases; the junior author, with a background in the fields of mathematics and child development, then checked and assembled the data for interpretation. Thus the chemical, biologic, and statistical interpretations were combined.

The discussion in this book is concerned with how physical and chemical growth and development interact and with the effects of their interdependent and co-ordinated metabolic actions on body composition during childhood (4–12 years, inclusive). During this period, when the body is least dominated by sexual factors, the impulse of growth is bringing about the gradual development of structure and the corresponding adaptation of the physiologic functions. At the same time the metabolically active protoplasm is approaching chemical maturity.

The various chapters describe the different measurements and

assessments—anthropometric, roentgenographic, constitutional, physiologic, and chemical—and how they are applied to evaluate and
predict trends in body composition of living children.

Since the original data were recorded, however, new procedures
for assessing body composition have been developed. These procedures, which were devised during World War II, have led to a
new evaluation of body composition in living adults. Thereby the
scope of physical anthropology has been expanded and extended to
include chemical growth and its relationship to physical growth and
physiologic function. We call this *chemical anthropology*. It is our
aim here to reinterpret our original data on children in terms of this
new concept. We believe that the results will provide essential information that has not been available heretofore and thus open up a
new and far-reaching field in the study of child development and
improved care of children.

ICIE G. MACY
HARRIET J. KELLY

Acknowledgments

In 1923 the senior author was intrusted with the responsibility of inaugurating and directing a research program in the newly created Nutrition Research Laboratories of the Merrill-Palmer School and the Children's Hospital of Michigan to further the aims of Lizzie Merrill-Palmer, widow of Thomas Witherell Palmer, United States senator from Michigan and ambassador to Spain under President Harrison. Mrs. Palmer, who died in 1916, stated in her will:

I hold profoundly the conviction that the welfare of any community is divinely, and hence inseparably, dependent upon the quality of its mother-hood, and the spirit and character of its homes, and, moved by this conviction, I hereby give all the rest of my estate for the founding, endowment and maintenance, in the City of Detroit, of a school at which girls and young women shall be educated, trained, developed and disciplined with special reference to fitting them mentally, morally, physically and religiously for the services of wifehood and motherhood, and the management, supervision, direction and inspiration of homes.

In addition to a research program in line with the purposes set forth by the Merrill-Palmer School, during the years from 1923 to 1931 studies of maternal function were pursued intently as the basis of child development and nutrition in relation to health. Inasmuch as these studies utilized the group of natural sciences which base their concepts on measurements of physical, mental, and emotional growth and development, with emphasis on metabolism, chemical growth, and nutriture, it was essential to include research workers in many scientific fields.

In 1931 the Nutrition Research Laboratories, which after seven years comprised a valuable accumulation of scientific data and equipment, were transferred to the Children's Fund of Michigan, a charitable trust created in 1929 by the late Senator James Couzens "to promote the health, welfare, happiness and development of children of the State of Michigan, primarily, and elsewhere in the world." The scope of the Research Laboratory was thus broadened in its efforts to establish a better understanding of the biologic

x *Acknowledgments*

processes of the mother and child, either of which is inseparably involved with the other.

The Research Laboratory, Children's Fund of Michigan, terminated April 30, 1954, in accordance with the trust agreement of the fund, but unfortunately before the staff had concluded the colossal task of assembling, evaluating, and making available even a small part of the interpretations of the long-term study recorded in *Nutrition and Chemical Growth in Childhood.* Since no provision was made by the fund for financial assistance to complete current unpublished materials accumulated under its direction and support, it remained, therefore, for interested individuals other than ourselves to evaluate the scientific merits of the inaccessible protocols. Because of the basic character of the research data and their possible applications to child health, financial support was mobilized for completing, recording, and distributing some of the remaining interpretations so that they might be available to research workers, practitioners, health authorities, and educators.

We are grateful, indeed, to the many individuals associated with the Merrill-Palmer School, the Children's Hospital of Michigan, the Children's Fund of Michigan, and the Methodist Children's Village who have contributed so much over the years to the work of our Research Laboratory. We are indebted to the community spirit of Detroit for the stimulating environmental conditions under which we worked. The wholehearted co-operation of the medical, chemical, biologic, and social science professions given to the organization and to the carrying-out of the experimental design of the research provided extensive data of broad scope. We believe that the results will reflect in full measure the support we have received and will contribute in turn to better understanding of child growth and care.

We are particularly grateful for the encouragement and support of the following individuals and associated foundations: Pauline Park Wilson Knapp, director, and the board of Merrill-Palmer School, for providing office facilities in a cordial environment; R. R. Williams, director, Williams-Waterman Fund, for voluntarily making the original survey of the status of the research at the closing of the Children's Fund in 1954 and for providing immediate funds to retain essential staff members for continuation of specific publications; Charles G. King, scientific director, Nutrition Foundation, Inc., for giving encouragement and providing a voluntary grant; the Kresge Foundation, for furnishing funds for editing and publishing protocols and their application to child health; H. E. Robinson, research director, Swift and Company, for contributing a grant; and the National Institute of Health for the Study of Rheumatic Diseases, for giving support to that phase of the study having to do with mineral metabolism, skeletal maturation, and bone density.

Special acknowledgment is given to the following former members of the research staff for their valuable contributions to the planning and development of the research program: Eliot F. Beach, director, Biochemical Laboratory, Metropolitan Life Insurance Company; Helen A. Hunscher, chairman, Department of Home Economics, Western Reserve University; and Harold H. Williams, chairman, Department of Biochemistry, Cornell University. We wish to acknowledge also the close co-operation and support of Genevieve Stearns, research professor, Department of Orthopedics, Iowa State University Medical School, whose constructive criticism has been most gratefully received.

Finally, we greatly appreciate the contributions of Vera Ruttinger, who gave valuable assistance in assembling and recording the statistical data; Dorothea Thorburn, who has helped in the preparation of the manuscript; and Constance Jones, who has typed the manuscript with such accuracy and care.

Contents

Contents

List of Figures

List of Tables

CHAPTER ONE

Basic Concepts of Growth

One of the great mysteries of life is the power of growth, that harmonious development of composite organs and tissues from simple protoplasmic cells, with the ultimate formation of a complex organism with its orderly adjustment of structure and function. Equally mysterious is that wonderful power of rehabilitation by which the cells of the body are able to renew their living substance and to maintain their ceaseless activity through a period, it may be of fourscore years, before succumbing to the inevitable fate that awaits all organic structures. This bodily activity, visible and invisible, is the result of a third mysterious process, more or less continuous as long as life endures, of chemical disintegration, decomposition, and oxidation, by which arises the evolution of energy to maintain the heat of the body and the power for mental and physical work. . . . Development, growth, and vital capacity all depend upon the availability of food in proper amounts and proper quality.

CHITTENDEN (1907)

THE THEME OF GROWTH

In trying to grasp the significance of the growing child, we are somewhat in the position of a person who hears a great symphonic work for the first time. We are awe-inspired, but we carry away only a general impression. With each additional hearing of a musical work, however, the details emerge from the mass and engrave themselves on our minds, until the basic harmonic progression or melodic theme of the composition becomes clear and links the musical action into a unity. Similarly, the more frequently we observe a child as he is being transformed into an adult and the broader the scope of our evaluations, the more we become aware of the basic progression and symmetry of growth which flow in accordance with biologic time and link the many physical, chemical, metabolic, and developmental processes into a functional unit. Increase in body size with accompanying changes of appearance are visible characteristics in a growing child. Changes in size, shape, and proportions form the basic theme of physical growth, in much the same way that melodic variations join together in musical action and form the theme of the

1

composition. Just as the theme of symphonic music may vanish from a recognizable leading role, so growth may disappear from view for a time, but sooner or later each will return in its original proportions or in some altered form.

HARMONY OF STRUCTURE AND FUNCTION

Growth of a child must be viewed with perspective; increase in visible size does not exist alone. We see change in size against a background of a progression of invisible chemical additions for enlargement of organs and tissues. It is these modifications in functional capacity and alterations in internal environment that permit full realization of the inherent capacity of the child for growth and development commensurate with its stage in the life-cycle. Nutrients must be consumed in the required amounts and proportions to meet the current needs for construction of protoplasmic mass and skeletal tissue and to provide for necessary modification of body fluids and chemical balances. Thus the harmonious blending of these physiologic processes and functions provides a favorable environment for growth to proceed unhindered.

Just as melody and harmony are not separate entities but contribute to the same musical process, so with growth: when there is symmetry of structure and function, a healthy biologic development usually occurs. If the requirements for growth are not fully met, however, the link between chemical growth and physiologic functioning is disrupted, and the inherent healthy pattern of growth and body composition cannot be maintained.

RHYTHM AND TEMPO OF GROWTH PROCESSES

Melody and harmony are not static qualities; similarly, there is no fixity in the components of growth. Growth processes flow with physiologic time. This is the third basic component of both music and growth, namely, rhythm. Rhythm denotes orderly movement in time. In growth it pertains to the duration and organization of the developmental pattern most closely allied with body progression toward maturity of structure and function. As rhythm is the heartbeat of music, so maturation in the child is the core of the body system in its steadfast pursuit of adulthood.

In a symphonic work we perceive certain changes in tempo and dynamics as the different movements are played. Study of the growth process reveals corresponding factors. We become intrigued by the interplay of chemical processes and their response to different internal and external environments, to metabolic performance, and to the rate of excretion of nutrients and waste. As we observe the transformation of the infant into the child, and of the child into the adult, we become aware of the relationship of these components to the tempo and the dynamic qualities of growth and development.

And, finally, just as melody, harmony, rhythm, tempo, and dynamics are the basic components of symphonic structure, the many factors in growth and development combine to produce the general construction of body form. One aspect of the body form is the *physical build,* which is based on the relationship of the parts of the body to the whole; the other aspect is the *constitutional type* in relation to physiologic function. Body form, which exists only in time, is of prime importance in the study of the structural outline during growth and development. When we learn to perceive the different physical patterns in relation to physiologic function, we become alive to the innumerable possibilities in the scientific study of children.

It becomes apparent that the stream of physical and physiologic growth is composed of many basic elements: changes in size, shape, and proportions of the body; harmonious modifications in structure and function of organs and tissues; and the rhythm of the maturation process, all progressing in varying tempo and dynamics. As we become better acquainted with the interplay between the physiologic and chemical manifestations as they relate to composition of the body, these components—tempo and dynamics—became more significant. We perceive them in a new relationship. With each succeeding re-evaluation of growth and development of the child in chronologic and biologic time, the child reveals itself afresh. The greater the technical knowledge, the more comprehensive will be the understanding of the manifold elements of normal growth and maturation and those deviations which may lead to disease or failure in growth.

INTERDISCIPLINARY RESEARCH

In the past half-century, and particularly in the past decade, dramatic changes and advancements in scientific knowledge have resulted from the rapid development of science. The greatest changes have come from the merging of the sciences into a concentrated study of man. No longer does the individual chemist, biologist, or psychologist confine his interest to one particular aspect of his own field. The boundaries that were thought to separate the various sciences have been pushed back almost to the point of obliteration. The individual scientist has become increasingly aware of the way in which his results may be conditioned by factors which he once thought properly belonged in another realm of science.

This new appreciation of the interdependence of the sciences has led to the development of multidisciplinary research, which has played such a vital role in the study of man. The co-ordination of techniques of the different sciences has permitted intensive concentration on many problems relating to man and his environment. In the field of biochemistry, for example, research can now be pinpointed on cells, organs, tissues, and the organismic whole through the use of diversified, more accurate, and more effective procedures scarcely dreamed of earlier.

The application of these *multi*disciplinary investigations to the study of man is still in the exploratory stage, but it has led to the effective integration of the results of many techniques of independent origin which we call *inter*disciplinary research. New methods are continually being brought into use, and old methods, some of which were formerly applied to the lower forms of life, are being adapted with greater significance to the study of the physiologic complexities of man.

Whereas formerly certain data on body composition were available only from the chemical analysis of cadavers, which were difficult to obtain and to analyze accurately, a new picture of body composition can now be presented which takes into account the dynamics of the living human being and makes possible the further breakdown of gross body weight with respect to water, fat, minerals, and protoplasmic mass (Behnke, 1941–42, 1953a, 1953b; Behnke et al., 1942). As a result, earlier data, many of which are still valid, must be reviewed in the light of this new scientific information of wider scope. Some established standards of reference will stand the test of time; others will have to be revised; still others will have to be replaced if an accurate and broader interpretation of the data is to be achieved.

Although any given standard of reference may be based on single, duplicate, or even multimeasurements of the body, the chances for error in establishing such a standard may be legion. This fact is exceedingly important, since some scales of observation have greater accuracy than others and since the degree of accuracy of the method must be taken into consideration in the interpretation and significance of the results. The role of the biostatistician, therefore, is an important one, both in the planning, organizing, and projecting of growth and development studies and in the evaluation and interpretation of the results. It was Darwin (cited in Tanner, 1953) who said: "A knowledge of mathematics added an extra sense to the scholar's mind; it is no less true that a knowledge of growth adds an extra dimension to the biologist's insight." The greater the amount and accuracy of data and the more diversified the interpretations and interrelationships to be studied, the greater the contributions of the mathematician may be in devising techniques for testing their significance, the validity of the assumptions made, and the results obtained.

The total human being is divisible only as a matter of arbitrary convenience for those who wish to observe. We have to specialize in order to be able to handle the materials that we must study. Some topics will readily be studied from a general health point of view; others, from a physiologic, morphologic, sociologic, or some other point of view. But the subject man forms a single integrated unit which cannot be broken down into components that are separately understandable, because the whole pattern has greater significance than the sum of its many parts. Nevertheless, the strategy of science, with its body of theory and techniques, may be used to attack problems concerned with man. All specialty sciences have their traditional ways of assembling and analyzing data, and the effectiveness of a science may be judged by the way its strategy actually solves problems and points the way to new research.

INTERNAL AND EXTERNAL FACTORS IN GROWTH

We grow, we grow up, we mature. What an individual becomes in the course of his development, however, is the resultant of two factors—heredity and environment. *Heredity* acts through *internal factors* derived from both parents to control the characteristics of the developing individual. *Environment* acts through *external factors* such as food. The final character of growth and development depends on the interaction between the genetic and environmental factors.

Just as an individual possesses a peculiar set of inherited characteristics as the basis of his life-pattern, so he is endowed and moves in individualized biologic time. Biologic and chronologic age may be very different, for the former may be modified from time to time during life. The rate of growth in biologic time may be altered as an individual develops in life, depending on the environmental influences that are brought to bear on him. Of even greater significance, segments of the body may grow at different rates in biologic time. Some changes are obvious because present scales of observation permit description; however, many physiologic processes and changes currently defy description. Thus, much consequential knowledge of growth is missing, owing to the dearth of precise methods of observing and identifying the interdependent processes involved in the enlargement of size and maturation of functions of the body.

Since it has not been possible to observe an individual person both intensively and extensively over more than a relatively brief interval of chronologic time, seldom is the full development recorded. For this reason, therefore, it becomes necessary to work within *man-made compartments of time* and to apply the most refined procedures that current conditions and resources will permit. In our studies of childhood we chose to apply successive batteries of diverse tests that reveal physical and chemical growth and nutritional and developmental changes over periods of months at various intervals in the life-cycle. Observation of a few individuals during their physiologic adaptation to growth and development under known circumstances provides results that may be interpreted in terms of the group—cross-sectional studies—and in terms of the individual child—longitudinal studies.

Life is a series of continuous progressive changes which start with conception and end with death. Living tissues are in a constant state of building and of tearing down. It is possible to describe certain phenomena in an organism, but *the "vital" phase of the living state cannot be explained.* Scientific laws of physics and chemistry depend on the fact that in these fundamental sciences identical results follow on identical causes. In growth, however, nothing is static. Identical conditions cannot be set up for different individuals or even for the same individual at different times.

The differences in the quality and intensity of the irreproducible biologic reactions brought about by environmental changes depend in large measure on the inheritance, physiologic state, and nutritive background of the individual. In addition, in his progress toward maturity the individual constantly changes in complexity and organization of mind and body. Hence no set of conditions in man is reproducible.

Growth of Different Kinds

In contrast with the cyclic, non-progressive, and, in general, much more rapid physiologic changes—for example, respiratory, circulatory, digestive, and nervous activities—which are directly essential for maintenance of life, the individual undergoes continuous developmental changes of growth and aging which are gradual and of different sorts and kinds. They cannot be detected or described by superficial inspection. As man is progressively modified in accordance with his particular biologic schedule, new mechanisms are continually coming into activity, and others are receding, so that he may live and cope with changing internal and external conditions as developmental alterations take place. As man grows, his organ systems are unremitting in their progress toward full performance of the physiologic activities peculiar to them in mature or adult life.

Some scales of observation will reveal gross changes, but for detection of the more subtle adaptations of the organs and tissues more refined chemical and biologic procedures must be applied. These new concepts of biochemistry, which envision a dynamic state of body constituents, have replaced the classic picture of a fixed system; nevertheless, the structural components of the organism retain a relatively constant pattern.

As the armamentarium of research on man is enlarged in scope and skilfully applied, the complexity and variability of dynamic functioning of the whole living mammalian organism will be resolved and thus make analysis of underlying mechanisms of growth and maturation a reality.

CHAPTER TWO

Design of the Investigation

The adult physical pattern is the outcome of growth, along lines determined by heredity but enhanced, dwarfed, warped or mutilated in its expression by the influence of environment in the adventures of life.

TODD (1935a)

EXPERIMENTAL ENVIRONMENT

An extensive and rigorous study of average healthy children must in its conception be predicated on maintaining study conditions which acceptably approximate normal physical environment, subject to the usual mental and emotional influences of daily living but at the same time allowing for the accuracy of control necessary to obtain consequential data. Control in such studies fundamentally is dependent on procuring the co-operation of children by stimulating their interest and pride in the work.

The emphasis in these studies was on the observation of a small group of children over a period of years rather than a large group for a shorter period. It has been shown that the results of such longitudinal studies bear out the data derived from studies of a cross-sectional nature and, in addition, add new information of great value to our understanding of the growth and development of children.

The data accumulated, which serve as the basis for this interpretation of chemical and physical anthropology, have been presented in *Nutrition and Chemical Growth in Childhood.* Volume I, *Evaluation* (Macy, 1942), describes the organization and maintenance procedures which were utilized in the controlled investigation of normal children between the ages of 4 and 12 years: the selection, standardization, supervision, and routine of the children; observations and determinations made; dietary intake and distribution of nutrients; gastrointestinal activity; chemical aspects of digestion;

energy metabolism and metabolic balances; and hematologic observations. Volume II, *Original Data* (Macy, 1946), details all the results of observations made; and Volume III, *Calculated Data* (Macy,
1951), presents many different types of statistical evaluations in
terms of various external body measurements, both successively and
cumulatively, for individuals and for groups of children.

These three volumes include data on both boys and girls, presented individually and as a group. In certain age groups, however,
girls were not represented. As reference to these volumes will show,
where sufficient numbers of boys and girls were available for study
within any one age group, the differences in the chemistry of their
growth were negligible. For this reason and to simplify the presentation, this monograph is based primarily on the data for boys, which
may be considered representative of childhood. Further verification
of this approach may be found in future publications which will
interpret the individual and sex differences in detail.

Although a detailed description of the experimental environment
is given in these volumes, a brief summary will be included here to
indicate the degree to which the necessary study conditions were
maintained and to provide some background for the interpretations
and conclusions to be presented.

The Methodist Children's Village in Detroit, a home for children
who are orphans or whose parents are unable to care for them, provided an unusually suitable environment for the experiment. It is
located only twelve miles from the Research Laboratory. Furthermore, the atmosphere of the Village is that of a home rather than an
institution. The fact that the children live in small groups in cottages
simplified the problem of isolating those chosen for the experiment
and of maintaining constant supervision.

In selection of the subjects, medical, school, and social agency
records were carefully studied to exclude those children conditioned
by any detrimental factors, congenital or acquired. Only those children were included whose personalities and dispositions indicated
that they would adjust to the environment and would be co-op-
erative. Finally, the children who were acceptable on these points
were given complete clinical examinations to determine that in
every physical and physiologic respect they were well within the

normal range for their age. A sufficient number qualified as normal so that alternates were available. In the first period of observation, eleven subjects were studied for 95 days; in the second period, 4 years later, eleven subjects were studied for 225 days. And, after another 4 years, seven of the same children took part in further studies for 55 days.

The children were settled in their cottage several weeks before the experiment actually began so that they became used to the various procedures. They were supervised by a capable and experienced housemother. Three trained young women assumed the responsibility for carrying out the many precise details of the experiment.

In this preliminary period the children became familiar with the equipment used in making various tests and measurements, with the food they were given and the manner in which it was prepared and served, and with the details of collection of excreta. At the same time their individual food requirements were established, and they were stabilized nutritionally. By the time the experiment began, the children were accustomed to their new environment and routine and also to one another and their adult companions. They were relaxed, unafraid, and unembarrassed, and they were able to cooperate enthusiastically.

Equipment was provided for making precise measurements of height and weight, anthropometric measurements, and determination of basal metabolism. Each child had his own dining-room utensils. All food was carefully weighed and measured before being served. Duplicate meals were prepared so that an amount of food equivalent to that eaten by the child, and prepared in the same fashion, could be measured and submitted to detailed chemical analysis. All excreta were collected, measured, and analyzed. Measurements were made under carefully controlled conditions and by more than one trained observer. In addition to these specific measurements, subjective observations were made of the children's emotional reactions to their daily activities.

Every effort was made to provide a normal, healthy, happy atmosphere within the experimental regimen. The children attended a private school on the Village grounds, where continuous observation could be maintained. They enjoyed play periods, parties, and special treats in recognition of their co-operation during the study. Appetizing meals were carefully planned to avoid repetition, although the same basic foods were used throughout the experiment. The children's general physical and emotional state was checked by a doctor, a dentist, and a psychologist. They appeared to be healthy and contented and even proud to be a part of the experimental study.

MEDICAL EXAMINATION

For each child chosen for study a complete medical history was available. In addition, the children were under medical observation throughout the experiment. The usual clinical analyses of the blood and urine were performed, and measurements of height and weight were made. Detailed discussion of these factors will be presented later. The physician also made many observations of a subjective nature, such as evaluation of muscle tone and condition of the skin, hair, eyes, mouth, and tongue. The dentist observed the condition of teeth and mouth. Although these factors cannot be rated on a quantitative scale, they do reflect general health status. The sum of all these observations gives some indication of the stage and symmetry of growth and maturation and, in addition, serves in the evaluation of the nutritional state of the child.

PSYCHOMETRIC OBSERVATIONS

The children were given various tests which indicated that they were of average intelligence. These tests were performed by psychologists not only before the study began, as one means of choosing the subjects, but also during the experimental periods.

It has long been recognized that emotional factors play an important role in the physiologic functioning of the body and that they must be taken into consideration in the study of physiologic function and chemical growth. Psychologic tests and emotional evaluations were made, indicating the general mental health and personality of the child, and daily observations of each child's social reaction to his environment were recorded by several independent research workers. In general, it was found that the children lived normally and happily under the experimental regimen.

PHYSICAL ASSESSMENTS

Anthropometric Measurements

In any study the selection of specific measurements which will be most useful and significant is important and will vary according to the purposes for which the study was undertaken. In the present work age, sex, and weight, together with the following linear body measurements and subcutaneous fat evaluation, formed the basis for physical assessments:

> Linear body measurements (centimeters)
> Recumbent total length
> Recumbent stem length
> Recumbent tibial length
> Shoulder (biacromial) width
> Hip width: intercristal, intertrochanteric
> Head: circumference, width, length
> Chest at nipple line: circumference, width, depth
> Upper-arm circumference
> Abdomen circumference
> Thigh circumference
> Subcutaneous fat: upper arm

Increases in body weight and height are generally considered criteria of growth and development and are readily measured with reasonable accuracy and without inconvenience to the child. It is common knowledge that healthy growth may take place at varying rates in different sections of the body or throughout the body as a whole, even though signs of change of weight or height may not be apparent. Although under some conditions and circumstances neither augmented weight nor failure to gain in body weight may be considered conclusive evidence of satisfactory or unsatisfactory chemical growth, weight is nevertheless one of the criteria most commonly applied in studies of children. There can be progressive enlargement of muscular, neural, and glandular tissues and skeletal formation, and yet the total body weight may remain unchanged, or even be reduced, because of loss of fat and adjustment in fluid balance. In other words, progressive gain in body weight is only a gross measurement of chemical growth and storage of nutrients. Different types of growth or gains in body weight are known to vary in chemical composition as well as in rate, and the accumulated weight may not be a direct measurement of storage of tissue-building constituents. Yet weight gain is important, in relation to age and height, to *total* gain or loss and to *rate* of gain or loss subsequent to disease or injury. Excessive weight gains tend to increase susceptibility to disease and may become a health hazard.

In measuring weight, many factors have to be considered. The accuracy of the scales must be checked by standard weights before and after each weighing. The most significant measurements are obtained when the individual is unclothed and in a fasting state, after urination, and, when possible, after defecation. As an additional check, readings should be taken and recorded by more than one person. Under these conditions experimental error may be reduced to the minimum, and the data obtained can be used with confidence in relating weight to the other aspects of physical and chemical growth.

In the measurement of height it was recognized early that, owing to the degrees of reliability and objectivity of observations, variations may occur which might be interpreted erroneously as true differences. For more than a century and a half it has been known that the body may shrink in height during the day (Scammon, 1927). Conversely, there may be a gain in stature after a night's rest (Curtiss, 1898; Redfield and Meredith, 1938) or even after an afternoon nap (Potter, 1925). The true cause of change in height during the hours of activity is not known, although some have considered muscle tone responsible. Shrinkage in height after sustained functional activity during the day may be related to muscular fatigue (Kelly *et al.*, 1943). Study of the chemistry of the muscle has shown that the varying decrease in muscle ability to respond which accompanies fatigue is due to a progressive loss of irritability and contractibility of the muscle. After a rest there is a restoration of muscle tone and irritability. In making height or length measurements, a collection of pseudo-significant data may result if differences in the relative amount of activity by the different subjects prior to measurements are ignored.

In the present study recumbent-length measurements of the nude children were made immediately on their waking in the morning

(Macy, 1942). In a special study of shrinkage in height another measurement was made just before retiring for the night (Kelly *et al.*, 1943). The average decrease in total recumbent length ranged from 13 to 18 mm. and represented from 1.1 to 1.6 per cent of the corresponding total lengths of the children. The younger children showed the greater losses in length referred to total length, but no relationship is evident between the length decreases and body weight, surface area, physical type, laxation rate, or basal heat production. The average differences found for recumbent total length of these children are comparable to those observed in children of similar age by other investigators. The mean differences between the morning and evening measurements of recumbent total and stem length for the children were 14.7 and 15.6 mm., respectively. These differences are approximately equivalent to a 3-month gain in recumbent length by the same children.

The decreases in recumbent stem length are usually found to be much less consistent than those of total length, owing to variations produced by slight differences in position and the shift of the fat pads in response to pressure against the buttocks.

Since the evidence indicates that measurements of recumbent total and stem lengths are more accurate than standing and sitting height and that morning observations immediately after a night's rest are more reliable, they have been used in this presentation of physical and physiologic growth.

The same degree of precision is required in making and recording the other linear body measurements which are used in conjunction with measurements of height and weight.

Skeletal Assessments

Roentgenographic studies provide an objective measure of physical development as it may be reflected in the bones. The records obtained on the bones depend primarily on growth of the area undergoing ossification and on the deposition of minerals in the growing area. The two processes may not keep pace with each other, nor are they always present together.

The introduction of this method of determining skeletal maturation permits discrimination between physiologic and chronologic age, which may be quite different in some individuals. Roentgenographic analyses permit assessment of skeletal ossification centers by observation of contour changes and by planimeter and caliper measurements, as well as determination of degree of epiphyseal fusion. The latest-appearing center gives a truer measure of maturation than an average value for all the many ossification centers (Todd, 1937). In addition to the evaluation of skeletal age, an assessment of the differential developmental symmetry of the several regions of the skeleton according to function can be made. The age equivalents of both the *most advanced* and the *least advanced* bone in the child's roentgenograms are plotted on graph paper, thus permitting a pictorial expression of the developmental symmetry. Roentgenograms are important supplements in research on general body development and also in clinical evaluation of nutritional status.

The criteria used in assessing skeletal status from roentgenograms of children in this study were as follows:

I. Skeletal maturation (anatomic age)
   A. Determination
      1. Bone contours as evaluated by Todd's technique applied to hand, elbow, knee, foot, hip, and shoulder
      2. Carpal area as applied to hand
      3. Greatest diameter of carpals, epiphyses, metacarpals, and phalanges of hand by Kelly's technique
   B. Assessments of uniformity of maturation of the individual bones in one or more areas of the body
   C. Interpretation and evaluation of superficial tissue, muscle, bone, trabeculae, ground substance, evidence of damage to blood supply, and anomalies
II. Bone density as evaluated by microphotometric technique

The speed of development of the most advanced bone serves as a yardstick for the child's potential rate of skeletal maturation. Skeletal symmetry depends on the degree to which the least advanced bone approaches this rate during the full course of its maturation cycle. These various methods of assessing skeletal maturity make possible comparisons of chronologic and physiologic age on the basis of physical and physiologic growth, nutritional status and metabolism, and physiologic function. An objective method of determining density of bone has been devised and applied to the same roentgenograms; this method will be presented in future publications.

Activity Assessments

Although the methods of measuring physical activity leave much to be desired in the way of specificity, we know that such activity has a considerable influence on metabolism. Children of similar ages living under the same environmental conditions may respond differently. Pedometer readings show that an active child may cover seven miles, whereas a quieter child may cover only two miles in the same interval of time. In addition, there is ample subjective evidence that points to large quantitative differences in physical activity of young children, some of which may reflect individual emotional reactions.

CHEMICAL ASSESSMENTS

Various methods have been used in evaluating individual and group differences in metabolic function and in physiologic adaptation to increased nutritional needs accompanying growth and development. Since the turn of the century, metabolic studies of children have included determinations of intake and utilization of nutrients. Direct chemical analysis of food eaten must be made with great precision for each subject if the results are to be correlated with biochemical and physiologic findings, such as blood levels, excretion levels, and retention levels. Evaluation of nutrient intake is basic and furnishes useful and valuable data on the intricate problems of growth and metabolism in relation to health. Alone, however, it does not determine nutritional status of an individual, because previous and current environmental factors may affect the nutritive state.

One of the critical tests of the adequacy of the diet for growing children is storage of nutrients in the body. Determinations of the absorption and retention of many essential nutrients were made on the same children for successive extended intervals of time between the fourth and twelfth years of age. On the basis of these measurements plus biochemical determinations of blood components representative of various developmental and functional processes and involving several body systems, assessments were made of nutritional status and progressive physiologic adaptation to the stresses of growth and maturation.

The quantitative chemical procedures for evaluating physiologic growth and other methodologies for judging gastrointestinal activity include:

1. Metabolic balances: analysis of food and excreta for corresponding time intervals; determination of body gain or loss of protein and minerals
2. Measurement of urinary excretion of the metabolites of proteins and minerals
3. Oxygen consumption; basal heat production
4. Hematologic evaluation
5. Other determinations: gastrointestinal activity; laxation rate; fermentation of complex carbohydrates in the alimentary tract; fecal composition and characteristics

Metabolic Balances

The dynamic flow and interplay of chemical and physical growth are attained through nutrients, metabolism, physiologic function, and physical, mental, and emotional maturation. True growth involves the accumulation of protoplasmic tissue and the sum of many physical and chemical changes that take place in the body systems during increase in size.

If we wish to study the chemistry of healthy growth, the first prerequisite is the preparation of the child by providing him with a well-regulated life within an environment judged by competent authorities to be satisfactory for his particular physical, mental, and social progress. He must be furnished with a dietary composed of adequate quantities of the known essential nutrients and in such proportions to one another as to permit satisfactory utilization by the body for whatever needs exist, and the period of preparation must be long enough to permit replacement or construction, if need be, of depleted or underdeveloped tissues and disposal of body surpluses, if these exist. Satisfactory preparation may be accomplished within a few weeks for one child in contrast to several months for another, depending on the possible extent of depletion, maladjustment, or hidden hunger characterizing the child and the rapidity and completeness of his response to the standardized procedures. Not until nutritional stability of the child becomes a reality within a well-ordered environment, where experimental errors in techniques and control have been reduced to a minimum, is it possible to observe with some degree of certainty the truly normal growth process as manifested by the various measures we have employed. Indeed, under prolonged observations the metabolic procedure, accompanied by many related and diverse physiologic and chemical observations, not only gives information on the total body growth but differentiates some of the subtle chemicophysiologic adjustments and trends that take place in the growth of soft and skeletal tissues.

The storage of nitrogen by a child who is provided with adequate energy to meet the demands of activity and growth is considered evidence of increasing protoplasmic mass in the body. Although we are accustomed to thinking of protein metabolism primarily in terms of nitrogen, the importance of nitrogen or nitrogen and sulfur in the form of specific essential amino acids for synthesis of the protein molecule has assumed even greater significance as the nutritional and structural significance of amino acids has become clear.

There are apparently numerous controlling factors operating to affect the rapidity of nitrogen storage. Conspicuous among these is the energy intake (Macy and Hunscher, 1951). Some of the factors do not operate continuously, and, therefore, the organism seems to oscillate in its nitrogen needs. Past nutritional history is dominant among all the influences causing variations in children's requirement of nutrients and ability to utilize them in nutrition and growth. Observations on the nutritional reconditioning of children (Stearns and Moore, 1931; Stearns, 1939) demonstrate the rapid initial response of the majority of children to improved diet and environment. Such results strengthen the belief that nutritional conditioning or reconditioning is in large part dependent on the extent and duration of previous dietary inadequacy, or malnutrition from other causes, and may indicate why some children respond rapidly and others slowly. An additional factor may be the specific physiologic demands of the particular epoch of life through which an individual is passing. Perhaps most important of all the factors producing variable response to procedures of reconditioning is the natural inherent variability among individuals in their capacity to respond.

General body growth can be measured in terms of chemical units. A storage of both positive minerals—calcium, magnesium, sodium, and potassium—and negative minerals—phosphorus, sulfur, and chlorine—accompanied by nitrogen demonstrates that muscular, glandular, nervous, fluid, and bony tissues are either enlarging or developing or that both processes may be taking place.

Calcium makes up a large proportion of the mineral cations stored and is the major constituent of bone. Bone construction, therefore, may be indicated by a storage of calcium alone, of total mineral cations, or of an excess of mineral cations in relation to anions. The type of growth taking place at any one time, however, will depend on age or state of growth, the quantity and proportions of nutrients in the dietary, the internal environment and nutritive stage, the state of endocrine balance which controls growth, the external environment, and physical activity.

Urinary Metabolites

In studying the laws governing the chemical composition of urinary excretion, it has been shown that the output of creatinine is more or less constant on a meat-free dietary but varies for different individuals and is largely related to body weight (Folin, 1905; Shaffer, 1908; Hunter, 1928; Horvath and Corwin, 1941). According to Folin, creatinine excretion is an indication of "endogenous" or cellular metabolism, whereas Shaffer considered it an indication of muscle mass. The muscle mass possesses a storage of high-energy phosphate in the form of phosphocreatine, which under physiologic conditions undergoes spontaneous hydrolysis whereby phosphoric acid is split off and the ring closes to form creatinine. Creatine itself loses water to form the same product. As a result of these two reactions there is a steady production of creatinine which cannot be used for any metabolic purpose and is therefore excreted in the urine. This process is largely independent of diet and exercise but is dependent on total body mass. There is an increase in both the absolute and the relative excretion of creatinine from birth to puberty, the rate of increase being greatest during the initial months of life.

The increase in creatinine excretion observed in the children in this investigation was parallel with both age and increase in body weight. Creatinine excretion is directly related to basal metabolism in children (Palmer *et al.*, 1914; Talbot, 1936). Urinary neutral sulfur excretion, although not strictly independent of diet, is closely related to metabolism of energy as well as creatinine excretion

(Brody *et al.*, 1934; Brody, 1945). The factors affecting the metabolism of energy also affect the excretion of neutral sulfur, but neutral sulfur is not definitely proportional to caloric production.

Oxygen Consumption and Basal Heat Production

The determination of the energy expended by the protoplasm of the body when all the modifying factors of activity, food, and environmental temperature are producing their minimal effects has become an integral part in the assay of the health status and growth of the individual. This determination of the basal or minimum heat production of the muscles and internal organs of the body includes that expended by the involuntary muscular activity of breathing, of the heart in the resting state, and of the smooth muscles of the alimentary canal. The test records the performance of the body at a specific time, under a given set of conditions which cannot be exactly duplicated on other occasions because of physiologic changes in the body. The relative proportions of metabolically active tissue—muscular, glandular, neural—and inactive tissue—fat, bone, water —in the body vary greatly with different individuals and may vary in an individual at different times. In the present study of children, however, differences of not more than 5 per cent were found in basal metabolic rate tests made within a 7-day period.

The tempo of change in the human body is a relative concept and may not be proportional to chronologic time. The records of oxygen consumption and basal heat production in children at different age levels emphasize this physiologic phase as an integral part of the whole problem of evaluation of growth and nutrition. Comprehensive studies on basal heat production of children have been published (Benedict and Talbot, 1921; Talbot, Nathan, 1936; Lewis *et al.*, 1937, 1943; Talbot *et al.*, 1937; Benedict, 1938; Talbot, Fritz, 1938).

The data of this investigation should have special significance in that the children were exposed to the same environment and to the same dietaries and were highly trained in their performance as subjects in physiologic studies. The basal metabolic tests were made immediately after the children awakened in the morning, after there had been a complete restoration of the muscle irritability and tone and a return to a relaxed condition. Thus the effects of muscular fatigue and shrinkage in height were avoided. As a result, the inter-individual variability was kept to the minimum. The results indicated that some children experienced stages of very rapid growth which were coincidental with an elevated basal heat production. Basal heat production is also closely related to excretion of urinary creatinine and basal nitrogen, and both are directly associated with the changing amount and function of protoplasmic mass.

Investigators have recommended various means of interpreting oxygen consumption and the resultant heat production. Some have recommended the interpretation of the results on the basis of age and height, others include weight, and still others recommend a combination of height and weight such as surface area.

Hematologic Assessments

The homeostatic characteristics of the human body are demonstrated through its great flexibility and dynamic qualities. Although endowed by heredity with a given capacity for growth and development, the body's attainment in this respect is modified from day to day by its external and internal environment. At the inception of disturbed physiologic states, the regulatory mechanisms are thrown out of balance. The results may be observed in changes in the retention of nutrients from the food intake and in the levels or distribution of urinary components and blood components.

Physiologic changes coincident with growth may be revealed by the components and structure of the blood, for the composition of this fluid is a determining factor in the physiologic state of the entire body. The origin and functions of hemoglobin and the formed elements of blood—red blood cells, white blood cells, and platelets—are quite different. The quantity and structure of each constituent provide an index of the status of the tissues from which it is derived, and in case of structural and functional changes within the body any or all four constituents may reflect alterations in the fluid matrix and tissues of the organism. In the synthesis of these important components of the blood there are certain determining, reacting, and participating factors to which all are subject.

Quantitatively, hemoglobin content, red blood cell count, and white blood cell count are independent of one another. In an interpretation of observations on the quantity of these blood components in children, it is necessary to consider age, sex, time of day, and activity, as well as the effect of specific environmental conditions and other physiologic factors. The differential leucocyte count contributes special information on the physiologic processes that are taking place in the body. The polymorphonuclear cells may reflect the status of the myelogenous systems; the monocytes, that of the reticuloendothelium system; and the lymphocytes, that of the lymphatic system.

Pertinent information on the character and activity of the hematopoietic system can be obtained through hematologic observations accompanied by certain physical measurements, thus giving valuable information on the type of red cell formation. These include cell volume, weight, diameter, thickness, water content, and specific gravity. The size and shape of the red blood cell, as expressed by volume, diameter, and thickness relationships, play a significant role in its physicochemical behavior and therefore its physiologic activity or efficiency, both of which are so important to nutritive success and efficiency in somatic structural growth and development.

The red corpuscle may undergo changes which may affect its physiologic activity and efficiency. The maturity of the cell is an additional factor to be considered. Reticulocytes and immature erythrocytes alter the chemical picture. Reticulocytes have an augmented metabolism as measured by rate of respiration, whereas erthrocytes have a high oxidative and glycolytic metabolism.

Physiologic activity is not confined to respiratory exchange. The term may be used to include all the processes of the living cell. Although oxidation is the function most emphasized, it is only one form of activity. Processes other than energy transformation have significance in the total physiologic activities of most cells. A consideration of the growth process in connection with minerals and lipids of the plasma, together with hematologic observations, offers evidence suggesting that the concentration of minerals may indicate the ability of the organism to maintain equilibrium in spite of changing structure and function, whereas the lipids may indicate the progressive stages of development during infancy and childhood (Erickson *et al.*, 1937*a*). Certain characteristic differences of the plasma lipid found in the neonatal period, childhood, and maturity suggest a fruitful field of investigation in extending present data and exploring other periods of development. The lipid composition of the erythrocytes is fairly constant for an individual and, in fact, changes very little from childhood to adulthood, thus indicating that the lipids are a more fundamental part of the structure itself and not so likely to be influenced by changes accompanying growth and by environmental conditions. The minerals of the erythrocytes are probably more mobile constituents and may reflect nutritional status and certain environmental influences such as diet. The possibility of using certain of the blood constituents as indicators of the stage of development during growth should be explored further.

Gastrointestinal Activity

There is no single method completely satisfactory for determining motility of the normal human gastrointestinal tract, although this activity has fundamental significance in both health and disease, as it affects the digestion, absorption, and utilization of food consumed. During growth, functional processes are continuously going on, but there is no exact procedure for determining when the gastrointestinal pattern has been fully established or how much variation in motility exists among children within a narrow age range, under standardized conditions of environment, habit, and food consumption, or whether there exists any relation between motility and the assimilation of nutrients.

In a study of the transformation of food into living tissue or into body activity, the wide variation in the gastrointestinal response among different individuals is important. Type and motility of the alimentary canal have long been recognized as prime influences on digestion and absorption. Many studies of the functions and activity of the gastrointestinal tract have been made in an attempt to discover some of the effects of its physiologic activity on utilization of the food elements needed to maintain adequate body nutrition. Investigations have been carried out to determine the role of the nervous system, the optimal rate of passage of ingesta through the gastrointestinal tract, and the effect of bulk and the form in which feces should be excreted from the large intestine. The complex nature of the problem of absorption has been presented by Verzár and McDougall (1936).

Metabolic-balance studies do not permit exact evaluation of the functioning of the gastrointestinal tract, because those elements in feces that are present as a result of incomplete digestion of food cannot be separated from those that have been absorbed from the upper intestine and excreted into the lower bowel. However, several types of individual determinations or combinations of several observations may be used to clarify the role of the gastrointestinal tract in nutrition and growth. Among these are: the number of bowel movements per day, or *laxation rate;* the time required for food to pass through the tract, measured by a carmine marker ingested with the food; the evacuation time of the tract and its component parts, measured by roentgenograms; and the mass, consistency, and gross constituents of the materials defecated. The urinary excretion of ethereal sulfur is also used as an indication of gastrointestinal function on the assumption that the phenol and indole derivatives which make up the bulk of this fraction arise primarily from the action of putrefactive bacteria in the intestine.

Three methods of study were used. (1) Serial roentgenologic examinations were made of the progress of test meals of barium sulfate in various media through the sections of the tract, to obtain an evaluation of the response produced by different kinds of food—milks of different types (Reynolds *et al.*, 1939), foods predominantly fat, protein, or carbohydrate—and the variation in type and speed of response at different times during childhood. These test meals were given at times when they would not interfere with metabolic-balance studies. Planimeter measurements of the barium shadows in the roetgenograms show the area of maximum longitudinal section of the stomach but are limited by not yielding a three-dimensional picture. Nevertheless, significant quantitative information may be secured. (2) The motility of the entire alimentary canal was studied from the records of the elapsed time between ingestion and defecation of a carmine marker given every fifth day for eight consecutive months. (3) The third method of study utilized the times, wet weights, and dry weights of daily defecations over periods of observation during which the children were given a known adequate dietary and maintained regular habits of sleep, play, work, and bowel movements. These three methods have enabled a coordinated study to be made of the mechanics of the digestive tracts of the individual children in relation to other physiologic factors influential in growth and development.

Roentgenoscopic—fluoroscopic—examinations permitted study of the size, shape, and position of the esophagus, stomach, and duodenal bulb and supplemented the procedures used to determine normality of the children (Macy *et al.*, 1940).

Our study of gastrointestinal activity showed that two children may have the same number of bowel movements per day but that one individual may eject the larger amount of feces which are bulky, soft, and unformed, whereas those of the other child may be hard and the fecal units bear haustral markings. Furthermore, although each child had a characteristic pattern of gastrointestinal activity, fluctuations in this pattern occurred from one period of observation to another, even when daily food intakes were constant in quality and quantity.

Results showed that the fermentation of cellulose and hemicellulose in the tract are closely related and that their rate of disappearance from the intestinal tract of healthy children with regular habits of elimination is characteristic for each individual. Children whose laxation rates indicate a slow intestinal tract digest more of these complex carbohydrates than children with more rapid tracts. Children having a higher dry weight of feces and a lower output of cellulose and hemicellulose, indicating longer fecal retention and more extensive fermentation, show higher levels of urinary ethereal sulfate. These findings substantiate the long-held belief that the level of urinary ethereal sulfate is related to fecal retention and intestinal putrefaction. It appears that an average of one bowel movement or more per day, with elimination in not more than thirty-six hours, results in a minimum absorption of toxic substances, as judged from the excretion of urinary ethereal sulfate. The increased fermentation of the complex carbohydrates, a decreased water content of the feces, a decrease in number of bowel movements per day, or longer food passage time as children approach maturity may be associated with growth in length of the intestine.

EFFECT OF EXPERIMENTAL REGIMEN

Under the design of the investigation, as described above, it was found that the children in the study fully met the criteria of healthy growth and development, as evidenced by the following observations:

1. The appetites of the children were satisfied under customary conditions of activity; that is, they consumed nutrients comparable to the National Research Council's *Recommended Dietary Allowances* (1953) for children of similar age, sex, and activity.

2. The children were healthy by all clinical examinations at the onset of observation; they showed an average increase in body size and maintained nutritional stability as the study progressed.

3. Total gains in length, weight, and body dimensions were satisfactory.

4. Skeletal size and structure equaled those of children of equivalent ages. The maturation rates were usual, with some children initially slightly retarded but later average; only one was considerably advanced according to chronologic age.

5. The children retained average amounts of nutrients from dietary intakes judged to be adequate for normal health and growth of children in the United States.

6. The gastrointestinal emptying time and laxation rates were usual for childhood.

7. Oxygen consumption and basal heat production were within normal limits for age and sex.

8. Urinary excretions of creatinine and ethereal sulfate were comparable to those of healthy children of like age, living under a similar environmental regimen.

9. Body fluids and tissues were within normal range, that is, blood and red blood cells.

10. The children were of average intelligence, with some a bit advanced and others lower, as is customary in childhood.

11. Normal interplay of emotional experiences was observed. The children lived in a happy environment, attended school, enjoyed freedom of play and activity, and participated in some of the usual home activities and responsibilities. They were exceedingly proud of being in the study group.

CHAPTER THREE

Physical Characteristics of Children

Science can only ascertain what is, but not what should be.
EINSTEIN (1950)

Various body builds or types were recognized early in history. Hippocrates stated, "Some are hollow, and from broad contracted into narrow; some expanded, some hard and round, some broad and suspended, some stretched, some long, some dense, some rare and succulent, some spongy and of loose texture." Bayer (1940a) pointed out that classic myth and classic art have symbolized her four distinguishable types: the long-limbed Diana, her hypofeminine build; the ideal Venus, her normal feminine; Helene of Rubens, her hyperfeminine; and the masculine Amazon, her virile build. Approaches have varied, depending on the interest of the investigator and the objective of the study. Bayer classified the girls in her study according to build and observed whether deviations in build have any similar bearing on weight and menstrual characteristics. Draper (1928) and Kretchmer (1925) considered abnormal cases and observed predominance of definite builds in each group. Draper's ulcer group was composed almost entirely of "long thins" and his gall-bladder group of "short thicks." Kretchmer's manic-depressive or circular group had a high percentage of the pyknic type, and his schizophrenic or dementia praecox group consisted largely of asthenic, athletic, and dysplastic cases.

Davenport (1926) stated that "the body does not 'grow as a whole' . . . but growth of the body is the resultant of several growth-promoting internal stimuli. These act at different times and upon different organs." This was described graphically by Scammon (1930) as four types of growth—general or skeletal, neural, lymphoid, and genital. As a result, the study of growth becomes a very complicated one. Not all individuals can be classified as definite

27

types, and, on the other hand, individuals who can be classified as a definite type do not necessarily have the same build throughout their growth period.

The revered master teacher and investigator T. Wingate Todd was rightly called the "catalyst in growth research" by his student W. M. Krogman (1951). Like Claude Bernard (1865), he emphasized the consideration of the individual as a whole and proposed three basic concepts of growth which involved (1) increase in dimensions, that is, size; (2) change in proportions; and (3) adjustment of parts. Todd considered increase in size as growth per se and change in size as development—modification of proportions with increasing maturity. The sum of the two was termed "developmental growth." Adjustment of parts included differentiation, that is, local growth in dimensions with consequent readjustment in relation to the several structural parts involved. Todd (1937) also considered the meaning of maturation:

During childhood we grow: that is we increase in dimensions or, less literally, we put on weight. But we also grow up. And when childhood is over and we are grown up we begin to grow older and ultimately we grow old. This business of growing up, growing older, growing old is quite different from that of growing: it implies progressive maturity, not increased dimensions. Maturity is not experience: it is that upon which experience imprints itself and without which experience does not register. . . . Progressive maturity is something which we all share, no matter what our size, no matter what our experience. . . . There is, in the concept of progressive maturity, another implication not found in growth or in experience, namely its inevitability.

PHYSICAL ANTHROPOLOGY

Medical, dietary, anatomic, and physiologic studies have been used to characterize interrelatedness of physical and chemical observations during growth and development in childhood. Although the processes of growth, development, and metabolism involve chemical reactions which result in the incorporation of new tissues into the body, either as additional or as replacement, chemistry alone cannot provide complete information. Physical measurements applied to the body as a whole, or to its component parts, are also essential in the evaluation of the structure and function of the organs and tissues and are closely associated with the chemical composition of the cells, the tissues, and the body.

Evolution and growth of the body are brought about by a sequence of physical, chemical, and physiologic adaptations. All dimensions of the body fulfil specific functions. Certain dimensions, such as length and girth, form the basis of evaluation of body size. All other essential dimensions—linear, areal, and volumetric—are also related to and defined in terms of body size. Physical metric measurements were derived to describe certain features of the body and the skeleton and, when applied to human beings, to describe the individual. Although physical measurements are useful for translating dimensions into growth patterns and biologic variability, there is an unfortunate lack of knowledge as to what the measurements already devised really mean in terms of function (Kroeber, 1953).

The measurements on which physical anthropology are based were chosen primarily because they are definable in terms of skeletal landmarks. Some landmarks or end points of dimensions being measured are difficult to identify or locate; direct measurements of distance between these joints may deviate owing to the different techniques and instruments used and to variations in posture and degree of chest inflation of the person who is being measured. All these factors must be taken into consideration in interpretation of the data.

Table 1 shows the average general physical characteristics of boys in our study for the 4–6-year, 7–9-year, and 10–12-year age groups. All averages for each of the age groups were determined in such a manner as to correspond to the midpoint of the age group. In the youngest children the anatomic development was slightly lower in comparison with their chronologic age, whereas in the older age groups the skeletal development had accelerated and even exceeded the chronologic age. As would be expected, the basal heat production, which represents the sum total of oxygen consumed by all the various and different organs and tissues, increased as the children grew older and larger in size. Both gross weight and standard weight also increased per se. Other standard body measurements showed the customary average increase in size with age.

PHYSICAL BODY-BUILD ASSESSMENT

It is a well-known fact that the body form of the infant is not that of a miniature adult. Changes in body size and proportions take place throughout childhood. Long-term studies have been made that present the over-all pattern of change in the shape of an individual by pictorial and graphic methods (Wilmer and Scammon, 1945; Boyd, 1955). An analytic study of growth involves primarily the numerical expression of the phenomena of growth by mathematical figures. Such an expression permits interpolation of values at definite intervals, which is required in the study of growth. It has

TABLE 1

AVERAGE GENERAL PHYSICAL CHARACTERISTICS

CHARACTERISTIC	AVERAGE AGE GROUP		
	4–6 Years	7–9 Years	10–12 Years
Age:			
Chronologic, months	59	95	131
Anatomic, months*	52	99	137
Basal heat production, Cal./24 hr.	983	1,061	1,399
Body weight:			
Gross weight, kg.	18.5	24.8	34.1
Per cent of standard weight,† on basis of:			
Chronologic age	100	95	98
Anatomic age	97	95	98
Standard weight, kg., on basis of:			
Chronologic age	18.5	26.1	34.8
Anatomic age	19.1	26.1	34.8
Stature:			
Total, cm.	109	127	141
Per cent of adult stature§	62.7	73.7	80.0
Stem length, cm.	61.5	69.1	77.0
Length:			
Leg (tibia), cm.	22.8	27.2	32.0
Head, cm.	17.1	18.6	18.6
Width:			
Shoulder (biacromial), cm.	21.2	23.6	26.1
Hip (intertrochanteric), cm.	19.5	21.7	....
Hip (intercristal), cm.	18.0	20.0	21.4
Chest (nipple line), cm.	17.8	19.6	21.9
Head, cm.	14.6	14.3	15.1
Depth, chest (nipple line), cm.	13.5	14.5	15.7
Circumference:			
Head, cm.	50.6	52.6	53.5
Chest (nipple line), cm.	55	59	66
Thigh, cm.	30	34	39
Abdomen, cm.	52	55	58
Upper arm, cm.	15.8	17.0	18.5
Surface area, sq. m.	0.746	0.942	1.167
Creatine nitrogen excretion, mg./day	140	142	100
Subcutaneous fat (upper arm)	....	32	21

* Greulich-Pyle Standards (1950), inspectional average.

† Pryor's height, chest, and hip-width tables (1943).

‡ Combination of actual adult stature and estimated adult stature according to Bayley and Pinneau (1952).

been emphasized that "the study of growth is the study of a moving point, and no method of measurement which does not allow us to measure the movement of a value in its relation to the movement of some other value or to the lapse of time can prove to be a thoroughly successful method" (White House Conference on Child Health and Protection, 1932*b*).

Descriptions of body form or build, like descriptions of all other biologic variables, must be assessed for their validity. Meredith and Culp (1951) point out the need for continuing research with children, with greater emphasis on investigations in which the primary data are metric to supplement the available studies of human form which have used inspectional judgment as their primary data. These investigators believe that the more objective approach to the study of body build, through the application of anthropometric ratios, provides descriptions of harmonic progressions of body builds which are superior to those offered by observational ratings or visual appraisal.

Numerous morphologic ratios have been developed and used to measure and describe, quantitatively or pictorially, the changes taking place during the progression of the total body in relation to its component parts as growth and development occur. Meredith and Culp (1951) state that, "in order to obtain biologically sound age trends from ratios, the same form of measurement data must be used in the numerator and denominator of the ratio." Table 2 presents the measurements used for determining the physical body types of the boys in our study and the anthropometric ratios we have used in describing the average morphologic status of the children at ages 4–6 years, 7–9 years, and 10–12 years. The total length of the body is divided into the leg length and stem length because they have different functions. The body width and depth are related to total length and to the changes that occur in the shape of the trunk.

The morphologic ratios used to express the relative position of length are composed of (1) leg length to stature and (2) the skelic index, or leg length to stem length. Both ratios indicate that the two older groups of children have a longer relative leg length than the 4–6-year age group. Boyd (1935) observed a similar trend when studying the surface area of the human body. In connection with her observations of changes in fetal and infant surface area she states, "This general pattern of the age progression in proportionate parts . . . definitely demonstrates the existence of a fundamental increasing gradient of growth in the fetal period from the head downward . . . and indicates its probable extension into the post-natal period."

TABLE 2

AVERAGE MEASUREMENTS FOR DETERMINING PHYSICAL BODY TYPES

MORPHOLOGIC INDEXES*	AVERAGE AGE GROUP		
	4–6 Years	7–9 Years	10–12 Years
Total body form:			
Leg-length indexes:			
Leg length/stature	44	46	45
Skelic, or leg length/stem length	77	84	83
Trunk-width indexes:			
Hip width†/stature	16.5	15.7	15.2
Hip width/stem length	29.3	28.9	27.8
Shoulder width/stature	19.4	18.6	18.5
Chest width/stature	16.3	15.4	15.5
Extremity-girth indexes:			
Arm girth/stature	14.5	13.4	13.1
Thigh girth/stature	27.5	26.8	27.6
Thigh girth/leg length	63.2	58.7	60.9
Ponderal index‡	2.43	2.30	2.30
Pelidisi§	92.6	90.9	90.7
Trunk form:			
Width, girth, and depth indexes:			
Hip width/shoulder width	84.9	84.7	82.0
Hip width/chest width	101.1	102.0	97.7
Chest girth/abdomen girth	105.8	107.3	113.8
Chest depth/chest width	75.8	74.0	71.7
(Chest girth minus abdomen girth)/stature	2.8	3.1	5.7

* Units used: kilograms for weight, centimeters for linear measurements, and all indexes multiplied by 100, including the Pelidisi.

† Intercristal measurement.

‡ $\dfrac{\sqrt[3]{\text{Weight}}}{\text{Stature}}$.   § $\dfrac{\sqrt[3]{\text{Ten times the weight (in grams)}}}{\text{Sitting height (in centimeters)}}$.

The trunk width in relation to total body length may be studied at different age levels by the application of anthropometric ratios of hip width to stature, hip width to stem length, shoulder width to stature, and chest width to stature. These morphologic indexes suggest that the body becomes narrower as age increases, with but one exception—that of the proportion of chest width to stature. The dimensions of the hip and shoulder increase less rapidly in relation to stature; therefore, the average percentages progressively decrease at successive age levels, though the changes are not significant (Table 2). Knowledge of dimensions of the body is thus directly useful in studies of growth, development, body composition, and physiologic function.

The extremity girth indexes—upper-arm girth to stature, thigh girth to stature, and thigh girth to leg length—no doubt are related to change in body composition. The arm girth and thigh girth are readily influenced by accumulation of fatty and muscle tissues. The average girth of the upper arm relative to stature decreases with age, but there is no consistent trend for thigh girth relative to stature and leg length.

The shape of the trunk of the child changes with increasing age and may be described by the measurements of width, girth, and depth indexes presented in Table 2. The ratio of hip width to shoulder width decreases during childhood, demonstrating that the shoulders grow more rapidly than the hips. The relationship of hip width to chest width shows no definite trend with age. On the other hand, the chest-to-abdomen ratio demonstrates that the circumference of the chest increases more rapidly in proportion to that of the abdomen. The ratio of chest depth to chest width decreases with age. This anthropometric ratio discloses a progressive decrease with age and a tendency for the torso to become less circular and more elliptical in cross-section as children advance in age.

The average anthropometric ratios presented in Table 2 suggest trends from a stocky to a slender build and from short- to longer-legged individuals as these morphologically normal children grew older. These findings are further substantiated by other measurements and ratios. The ponderal index of $\sqrt[3]{\text{weight}}$ to stature was used in preference to either the index of $\sqrt{\text{weight}}$ to stature or of weight to stature, since it is believed to present a biologically sound age trend derived from ratios (Meredith and Culp, 1951) and is appropriate for properly nourished individuals. The ponderal index provides further evidence that there was a tendency for the average stature of our children to increase more rapidly than the cube root of the weight during childhood, thus confirming the change in physical body type from the stocky to the more slender build, as observed through the use of other anthropometric indexes. Von Pirquet considered the cube of the sitting height as a measure of the weight of a normal person. He devised the Pelidisi, which is the ratio of

$$\frac{\sqrt[3]{\text{Ten times the weight (in grams)}}}{\text{Sitting height (in centimeters)}}$$

The average Pelidisi of boys in our study for the 4–6-year, 7–9-year, and 10–12-year age groups were 92.6, 90.9, and 90.7, respectively. The figures support the conclusion that the children were not obese and grew slender with increasing age.

Wetzel (1943*a*, 1943*b*, 1943*c*) has formulated a grid based on the relationship of height to weight and divided into regions or channels which distinguish between the various weight status groups as obese, lean, and average. The grid serves as a device to observe the changes in weight status. The Wetzel Grid was used in further assessing the physical condition of our children (Table 3). That the average child is growing more slender at the older age levels is illustrated by the fact that the younger children fall within the A_1 physique channel, whereas the children of ages 7–12 take their places in the B_1 physique channel.

Girls observed in the study followed a similar course in physical body type. As a matter of fact, for practical purposes the normal boys and girls aged 4–9 years could be considered together.

Physique Assessment

The appraisement of the physique of a child requires an evaluation not only of his physical status at a given moment but also of his progress. Anthropometric measurements describe the individual and give an analytic expression to individual differences. They are of considerable consequence in the evaluation of constitutional differences, that is, "The total of all the morphological and functional characters by virtue of which an individual differs from other individuals" (Viola, in Tanner, 1953).

Table 3 presents the methods used in the appraisement of physique. The assessment of body physique is a determination of actual possibilities or capacity of the individual child and is a numerical expression of the degree to which these possibilities are being realized.

Increase of external measurements with age is to be expected; but did our children retain their relative position within their age group? To check this, their measurements were compared at each age interval with the recognized standards of Helen Pryor (1943) and of Stuart and Meredith (1946). Gross weight, compared with Pryor's standard based on height, chest width, and hip width, showed no trend with age and was within 5 per cent of her normal. Comparisons with the Stuart-Meredith standards for gross weight, stature, and hip width agreed within 8 per cent and, with the possible ex-

TABLE 3

AVERAGE APPRAISEMENT OF PHYSIQUE

MEASUREMENT OF BODY SIZE*	AVERAGE AGE GROUP		
	4–6 Years	7–9 Years	10–12 Years
Gross weight/standard weight†	100	95	98
Gross weight/standard weight‡	96	92	97
Stature/standard stature‡	98	98	98
Hip width/hip width standard‡	99	97	95
Physique assessment§	A₁	B₁	B₁
Upper-arm subcutaneous tissue/standard‖		121	78
Upper-arm girth/standard‖		101	105

* Indexes are multiplied by 100.
† Standard weight on basis of chronologic age (Pryor, 1943).
‡ Standard measurement (Stuart and Meredith, 1946).
§ Wetzel (1943)—physique channels.
‖ Franzen (1929).

ception of hip width, displayed no trend with age. It may be assumed, therefore, that the children retained their relative position within the three age groups.

Franzen (1929) presented standards for upper-arm girth and subcutaneous tissue. Compared to these standards, the upper-arm girth of our children was within 5 per cent of normal. The subcutaneous-tissue measurements were more variable but within normal levels.

SKELETAL ASSESSMENTS

Before the roentgen ray was discovered in 1895, little was known about skeletal growth other than the realization that the bones change in size and shape and that growth stops when maturity is reached. The earliest study, that of J. W. Pryor in 1905, dealt with the appearance of the carpals and epiphyses of the wrist and hand. In this and in later papers (Pryor, 1908, 1928), standards were set up for the average time of appearance of centers of ossification. Rotch (1908–10*b*) and Rotch and Smith (1910) listed thirteen stages of development rather than age groups. Age equivalents were then given for each stage. One great disadvantage of standards based on "age of appearance" is the limited age range. Pryor recognized this inadequacy and formulated additional standards based on the time of complete fusion.

Another technique for studying skeletal growth is the measurement of the size of the bones in terms of area, perimeter, or diameter. Baldwin (1921) measured the perimeter by means of a map tracer and protractors and the area by tracing the bone on cross-sectional paper and by a planimeter. Later, measurement of the longest diameter was added (Baldwin *et al.*, 1928). Recognizing individual differences in size of wrist and hand, Baldwin tried various indexes of osseous development and established a procedure based on measurements of bone size considered in relation to wrist width and wrist area.

Carpal bones have long been accepted as representative of ossification of the body as a whole. Using the roentgenograms of the hand and wrist, Kelly (1937) developed a single estimate of anatomic age, known as the CM/WD index. This is the sum of the greatest diameters of the eight carpal bones, the widest diameter of the radial and ulnar epiphyses, and the broadest width of the epiphyses of the first four metacarpals, divided by the average diameter of the wrist (Table 4). The advantage of the Baldwin and the Kelly methods is the objectivity of the measuring techniques and the simplicity of the equipment required. The Baldwin method uses a planimeter; in the Kelly method only a caliper or a ruler is needed.

The Todd method (Todd, 1937) of assessing skeletal age combines various methods and is based on the bone form or modeling of the bone cortex in the region of the joints—hand, foot, knee, elbow, or shoulder. The standard of reference consists of a series of roentgenograms of suitable joints which illustrate successive degrees of skeletal maturity which may be expected before the bone attains its adult size and form.

We were fortunate in having the close collaboration of Dr. Todd from the outset of our studies and, later, the co-operation of Drs. Pyle, Greulich, and Hoerr. The roentgenograms of our children were taken under the supervision of Dr. Todd and assessed by him and his associate, Dr. Francis, by his inspectional method of skeletal development. This assessment is based on the form of the bone and is made by timing the changes through which the articular surfaces

TABLE 4

METHODS FOR ASSESSMENT OF SKELETON

ASSESSMENT	AVERAGE AGE GROUP		
	4–6 Years	7–9 Years	10–12 Years
Chronologic age, months	59	95	131
Skeletal maturation, months:			
Hand:			
Baldwin (1921, 1928)	64	99	143
Flory (1936)	38	79	112
Kelly (1937)		102	134
Todd (1937)	53	101	139
Todd (1950)*	52	99	137
Greulich-Pyle (1950)	55	98	137
Foot, Todd†	55	100	143
Elbow, Todd†	53	99	141
Knee, Todd†	59	101	143
Hip, Todd†	54	102	152
Shoulders, Todd†	57	99	138
Average of six centers†	55	100	140
Skeletal size, cm.:			
Total height	109	127	141
Stem length	62	69	77
Hip width, intertrochanteric	19.5	21.7	
Hip width, intercristal	18.0	20.0	21.4
Shoulder width, biacromial	21.2	23.6	26.1
Head circumference	50.6	52.6	53.5
Skeletal growth, daily accumulation, meq.			
Calcium retention	9.7	6.6	13.2
Excess base retention	8.4	9.1	9.9

* Greulich-Pyle Standards (1950), inspectional average.   † Unpublished atlases.

of the bone and the epiphyseal cartilage plate progress to form the joints of the body. The age equivalents of the several bones are reduced to an average and compared with the child's chronologic age. Drs. Todd and Francis assessed the hand, using the Todd (1937) Atlas, and the foot, elbow, knee, hip, and shoulder by his unpubished standards.

The Todd technique was extended by Greulich and Pyle (Hand

Atlas, 1950) and by Pyle and Hoerr (Knee Atlas, 1955). A revision of the Hand Atlas and the atlases for the elbow, hip, and shoulder are in preparation for publication. Since Todd's original *Atlas of Skeletal Maturation* was published in 1937, however, many additional roentgenograms on children have been accumulated, thus permitting the formulation of a New Standard of Maturation on a more satisfactory basis and the correction of recognized shortcomings that had originated because of too few roentgenograms at certain age levels. In addition, the methods of Greulich and Pyle and of Pyle and Hoerr are based on the selection of different osseous centers for inclusion in the over-all average skeletal assessment of a specific joint.

The initial assessments of the roentgenograms of our children made by Dr. Todd, prior to the publication of the *Atlas,* were recorded in Volumes I and II of *Nutrition and Chemical Growth in Childhood* (Macy, 1942, 1946). The Greulich-Pyle Standard was applied by Dr. Pyle to the roentgenograms which had been assessed by Drs. Todd and Francis and recorded in Volume III (Macy, 1951). Slight differences recorded in the assessments of skeletal age may be noted, depending on the standard used in making the comparison and the osseous centers selected for assessment of a specific joint. A comparison of the evaluations made by the Todd and Greulich-Pyle Standards using the inspectional and arithmetic mean as applied to the roentgenograms of one child serves to illustrate the discrepancies that may arise in the average assessments of skeletal age of bones of the hand and wrist:

Chronologic age, months	47	68	95	106	120	146	183
Average assessment of the hand:							
Todd (1937), inspectional average	51	81	121	129	134	153	186
Greulich-Pyle (1950), inspectional average............	47	78	112	126	140	153	179
Greulich-Pyle (1950), arithmetic mean..............	49	78	111	125	140	156	183

Roentgenographic studies also provide an opportunity to examine localized areas for mineral content, texture, structure, and density of bones (Todd, 1937). Todd's inspectional method was extended by Pyle, who based her interpretations on the following classifications: thickness of subcutaneous tissue, bulkiness of muscle, size of bone, coarseness of trabeculae, density of ground substance, evidence of damage to blood supply, and anomalies, such as "gaps" in a primary center. The readings of the roentgenograms of our children were made by Pyle on the basis of these criteria and have been recorded in detail (Macy, 1951). In addition to the inspectional method for determining skeletal density, the photoelectric microdensitometer method was applied to our children by Mack *et al.* (1949); the data will be presented in future publications. Roentgenograms have also been used to evaluate the shadows of subcutaneous fat, bone, and muscle-tissue components of the calf of the leg (Stuart *et al.*, 1940; Stuart and Divinell, 1942; Reynolds, 1944, 1948).

Assessment of skeletal maturity, in association with anthropometric measurements, has served a useful purpose in the study of physical and mental progress, metabolism, and physiologic function. Deprivation owing to restricted or unbalanced diets, disease, or injury, as well as hereditary and environmental influences restricting the endocrine balance permissive of normal growth, may thwart the growth impulse and change the character of chemical growth to such an extent that the bones will be inferior and irregular in mineral composition, and this condition will be reflected in the character of the maturational progress.

Many chemical and physiologic activities are involved in the development of bone structure. Each stage in this development is based on preceding stages, and the entire pattern may be delayed or interrupted at any time. Skeletal growth results when bone salts are molded into a hard cortex as a result of changes in cell complexity. Generally, growth is characterized by an increase in bone size, but this increase in size is not necessarily equal throughout a bone. Maturational changes and changes in density also occur, but they, too, are not always accompanied by an increase in size. And bone, unlike other body tissues, is unique in that it cannot decrease in size during growth. The density, however, may change (Todd, 1937).

Anthropometric measurements made on the human body or skeleton provide information on somatic size differences, on changes in size and proportion in the bodies of children in biologic time, and on somatic deviations from norms due to internal or external environmental causes, injury, or disease. Their value in human biologic work depends on the use of proper techniques of measurement and the precision with which they are applied, the accuracy of the methods for recording and tabulating the results, and the integration of these results with data on chemical growth and development.

Studies of growth are being enriched by the simultaneous observations of changes in external shape and in skeletal development and by a variety of objective and inspectional measurements of metabolic activity, body components, and physiologic functions. It has been stated that "studies of this sort, coupled with information about changes in physiological function during the growth of the child, will do more than anything else to bring together classical human genetics and constitutional work, to the mutual benefit of both" (Tanner, 1953). In this connection, studies of skeletal shape and size furnish significant data on body build and on constitution and promise salient information which can be related to body composition and physiologic function.

As pointed out by Washburn (1953), whereas the new physical anthropology of today "aims to enrich the study of the past by a study of the present, to understand bone in terms of function and life, the old tried to reduce the living to a series of measurements designed to describe bones." Appreciation of the importance of dividing body structures into their integral parts, based on a recognition of their anatomic function in the living individual and of the different adaptive mechanisms involved, has broadened and vitalized the studies of growth and opened up new vistas never before considered. Quantitative measurements of the different components of the body, as a whole and in localized areas, of the size and proportions of the body form, of the many inherent skeletal parts and areas, of the numerous metabolic processes of tissues and organs, and of physiologic function permit an initial piecing-together of the life-pattern of growth and development in broader scope than has heretofore been possible. The advancement in knowledge so rapidly being accumulated in all the physical, biologic, and sociologic sciences will vitalize and advance the science of man.

CHAPTER FOUR

Metabolic Fate of Nutrients

Life is action and change; nothing is ever exactly the same from one moment to the next. The human mind, conditioned by its non-living environment, finds great difficulty in comprehending an ever-changing universe in which nothing can be kept stable for examination, in which the very act of examination alters the behaviour or even terminates the existence of the object to be studied.

LEE (1950)

Food is man's first requirement. There can be no growth or life without continuous consumption of food day after day, month after month, and year after year. Inquiry into physical and physiologic growth cannot be fully satisfied by the study only of food eaten or by investigation of the influence of dietary on body size. The metabolic fate of the organic and inorganic components must be studied in equally great detail in relation to physical and physiologic functions.

NUTRIENT INTAKE

Food is necessary for health and well-being at all times throughout life, but dietary quality and quantity have special significance when the body is subject to the augmented nutritive requirements that accompany the physiologic activities of growth or recovery from deprivation, injury, or disease. Growth of the structures and maintenance of the physiologic functions of the body require that all essential nutrients be included in the diets of children. Concepts of the composition and role of foods have changed with the rapid development of the science of nutrition, considered by Mendel (1923) to be "the chemistry of life."

The nutritional and physiologic condition of the body is the result of a chain of past experiences involving food intake, the processes of its utilization, body functions, endocrine balances, physical environment, attitudes, and social conditions. The prerequisite to a healthy life is provision of a food supply furnishing all the nutrients necessary for structural and functional activities in an environment permitting full utilization of them. Under such conditions the individual enjoys also that quality of resilience which enables him to respond positively to the ups and downs of daily life. It has been stated (Elvehjem and Krehl, 1947) that "one might define, as the optimum goal of the nutritional biochemist, the development of a diet which supplies all nutrients in respect to kind and amount and in proper state of combination for all physiologic processes from conception to the death of the organism. In addition, the adequate diet must contain a minimum of injurious (toxic) factors. Such a diet would indeed be balanced, and any important deviation downward from the proper amount of a nutrient would lead to one well-known kind of imbalance, reflected as deficiency disease"—or nutritional failure varying in severity over a wide range. Optimum nutrition no longer is construed in the narrow meaning of "absence of obvious disease" but expresses broader and more positive attributes such as stamina, efficiency, reserve, and capacity.

The fact that an individual appears normal does not mean that all is well nutritionally and physiologically in his cells, organs, and other tissues or even in the body as a whole. There is reason to believe that many children are getting less than 50 per cent of the essential nutrients necessary for optimal health (*Inadequate Diets,* National Research Council Bull. 109, 1943). Of the forty-three million children under the age of 18 years in this country (Metropolitan Life Insurance Company, 1953), it is probable that the percentage of individuals who are inadequately nourished is as great among children as it is in the entire population. On this basis, fifteen to thirty million children are improperly fed. The problem is one to be solved only by both preventive and corrective measures. For prevention, the production and distribution of sufficient food must be maintained. In order to conserve its original nutritive value, food must be carefully prepared and served. To achieve this, dietary education must be both intensive and extensive. For correction, the prime need is for greater skill and better methods of detecting malnourishment and deficiencies, followed by a careful feeding program.

Prolonged use of submarginal diets may force a body into a lowered nutritional and functional state. Depressed nutritional and physiologic conditions may develop during any epoch in the life-

cycle and may influence the health and dietary requirements in succeeding periods. Under- or misfeeding may occur over short or long
intervals without causing the body to make a physiologic protest,
but the results are demonstrated by poor nutritional status and
bodies "conditioned" to a poor diet. The physiologic demands of
growth may be conditioning factors, since they increase the chemical
needs of the body. Therefore, every individual has a characteristic
physiologic capacity to utilize and store chemical elements from
ingested foodstuffs. This capacity is determined by heredity, eating
and elimination habits, and physical and mental status. Once an
individual has developed malnutrition, he must be provided with
enough of the proper foods to restore him to a balanced nutritional
condition and to enable him to maintain that condition. The period
of time needed to bring the individual back to a healthy level may
vary tremendously. In childhood it can often be accomplished in a
relatively short time, depending on the severity of the condition.
During adolescence, on the other hand, a longer period is usually
required, owing to the many additional stresses experienced during
that phase of life (Stearns, 1951).

As judged by the National Research Council's *Recommended
Dietary Allowances* (1953) and by use of the metabolic-balance
method of determining assimilation of nutrients, the children in this
investigation received adequate dietaries to meet their body needs.
The average daily intake of various dietary factors by these children,
aged 4–12 years, is shown in Table 5, with the corresponding National
Research Council's recommendations for optimal dietary where
available. For another important compilation of the daily nutrient
allowances for childhood in the United States, *Standard Values in
Nutrition and Metabolism* (Albritton, 1954), should be consulted.
The diets given supplied average numbers of calories equivalent to,
or slightly above, the recommended allowances. Figure 1 shows the
distribution of protein and energy in the dietary. The subjects were
within normal range in height, weight, physique, skeletal development, and habits.

In evaluating a dietary for practical use, the final test is whether
the foods supply the chemical needs of the body simultaneously
and continuously. By means of diets composed of natural foods in
common use, served under living conditions as nearly normal as

TABLE 5

AVERAGE DAILY NUTRIENT INTAKE

MEASUREMENT	4–6 Years				7–9 Years				10–12 Years			
	Total	NRC*	Per Kg.	Per Sq. M.	Total	NRC*	Per Kg.	Per Sq. M.	Total	NRC*	Per Kg.	Per Sq. M.
Weight, kg.	18.5	18			24.8	27			34.1	35		
Body surface area, sq. m.	0.746				0.942				1.167			
Stature, cm.	109	109			127	129			141	144		
Water, ml.	1,332				1,452				1,838			
Energy:												
Heat of combustion, Cal.	1,803		99.7	2,443	2,051		83.4	2,181	2,443		72.6	2,080
Metabolizable, Cal.	1,666	1,600	92.1	2,257	1,889	2,000	76.9	2,009	2,244	2,500	66.7	1,910
Total food (dry wt.), gm.	357				403				477			
Protein (N×6.25), gm.	61.2	50	3.32	81.9	70.7	60	2.86	75.1	82.2	70	2.42	70.0
Carbohydrate, gm.†	192		10.6	260	209		8.5	222	235		7.0	200
Fat, gm.	70.7		3.9	95.9	83.8		3.4	89.1	107.8		3.2	91.4
Calcium, mg.	807	1,000	44	1,080	947	1,000	38	1,005	1,059	1,200	31	905
Calcium, meq.	40		2.2	54	47		1.9	50	53		1.6	45
Magnesium, mg.	286		15.4	384	299		12.2	319	394		9.5	277
Magnesium, meq.	23		1.3	32	25		1.0	26	27		0.8	23
Sodium, mg.	2,129		115	2,853	2,436		98	2,578	3,004		88	2,556
Sodium, meq.	93		5.0	124	106		4.3	112	130		3.8	111
Potassium, mg.	2,582		140	3,465	2,888		117	3,066	3,486		102	2,966
Potassium, meq.	66		3.6	89	74		3.0	79	89		2.6	76
Phosphorus, mg.	1,114		60	1,493	1,285		52	1,362	1,592		47	1,358
Phosphorus, meq.	65		3.5	87	75		3.0	79	92		2.7	79
Chlorine, mg.	3,370		182	4,516	3,751		152	3,983	4,396		129	3,744
Chlorine, meq.	95		5.1	127	106		4.3	112	124		3.6	105
Sulfur, mg.	681		37	913	786		32	832	1,009		30	859
Sulfur, meq.	42		2.3	57	49		2.0	52	63		1.9	54
Total minerals:												
Positive, meq.	222		12.1	299	252		10.2	267	299		8.8	255
Negative, meq.	202		10.9	271	230		9.3	243	279		8.2	238

* National Research Council, *Recommended Dietary Allowances* (1953).
† Calorie basis.

possible, it was demonstrated in several ways that the chemical needs of the children in our studies were met.

The differences between the analyzed and calculated values of diets with respect to all nutrients are important. Because of the exploratory nature of this investigation into the relationship between diet and physical and chemical growth, it was necessary to employ the most exact quantitative procedures available. For this reason, only analyzed values of diets were used, since they give a more accurate assessment than those calculated from standard tables and,

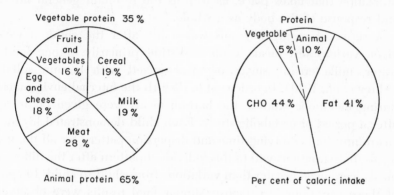

Fig. 1.—Distribution of dietary

therefore, contribute to a more precise evaluation of growth and nutrition which is essential in any interpretation of chemical anthropology.

GASTROINTESTINAL ACTIVITY

The primary functions of digestion are the preparation of food for passage through the alimentary canal and cleavage of the food materials into substances which can be assimilated. Digestion and absorption of food depend on mastication and mixing with salivary secretions, the type and condition of the food in the stomach and subsequently in the intestinal tract, and the length of exposure to the various digestive and absorptive processes. Many factors are interrelated in the activity of the alimentary canal: the size of the meal ingested, its consistency and contents, the nutritional state of the individual, and the emotional and environmental conditions to which the individual is subjected at the time.

Mendel (1904) pointed out that "the physician should recognize in the study of alimentation something more than the mere consideration of the solvent action which the digestive secretions can exert . . . [it is—] in the appreciation of the cooperative working of many functions—an ordered march of events." In any metabolic study it is important to consider the characteristic biologic pattern for the different segments of the alimentary canal, the interdependence among various physiologic tissues in the biochemical changes which proceed within the tract, and the absorption and utilization that takes place, as well as the resultant general fitness and response of the body as a whole.

A series of roentgenograms was made after the children were given various test meals, each consisting primarily of one food—water, milk, cream, sugar, or meat—mixed with barium sulfate (Macy *et al.,* 1940). In order not to disturb the internal environment during metabolic studies, the barium meals were given before or after a period of metabolic study. Each child demonstrated his own gastrointestinal emptying time and dispersion pattern for all the test meals, but variations within this individual pattern after the different meals were even greater than variations from child to child. In spite of these variations in response, similar final results were observed for all the children. The subjects who tended toward faster gastric emptying showed a slower passage through the intestine. Those whose stomachs emptied less rapidly demonstrated faster transit through the intestine.

The water meal produced the most consistent and constant reaction within both stomach and intestine (Table 6). The milk, cream, and sugar meals were subject to an initial delay in gastric emptying. In comparison with the progress of the water through the intestine, the milk mixtures were slightly delayed, and the cream meal considerably retarded. The meat meals, containing both protein (7 per cent) and fat (3.5 per cent), produced the greatest delay in gastric emptying but made more rapid progress through the small intestine. After the initial delay in gastric emptying, the carbohydrate meal filled the entire small intestine very rapidly, and at the same time the stomach increased in size, indicating rapidity of action of a humoral mechanism which reacts to bring stomach content to isotonicity by osmotic induction of water into it. There were individual differences among the children which will be considered in detail in a later publication.

The body, which is organized for homeostasis, always attempts to bring ingested fluid to the isotonic state; consequently, introduction of hypertonic sugar solution into the stomach is followed by a rapid increase in the volume of gastric content and a decrease in sugar concentration. This can be demonstrated by a comparison of the volume change of stomach contents when inert water and carbohydrates are used as conveyors of the barium. Planimeter measurements were made of the barium shadows on the roentgenograms

TABLE 6

AVERAGE GASTROINTESTINAL RE-
SPONSE OF CHILDREN TO TEST
MEALS OF BARIUM IN WATER,
MILK, CREAM, MEAT, AND CAR-
BOHYDRATE MEDIA*

Motility	Hours
Gastric emptying time:†	
Water meal.................	1.9
Milk meal..................	3.1
Carbohydrate meal...........	3.3
Cream meal................	4.8
Meat meal.................	5.0
Jejunum emptying time:‡	
Water test meal.............	2.4
Milk test meal..............	3.4

* Determined roentgenologically.
† Macy (1942).
‡ Macy *et al.* (1940).

of the stomach, taken 12 minutes after ingestion of the inert water-barium mixture and after ingestion of an equal amount of a carbohydrate-barium meal. A carbohydrate meal caused a significant increase in the average size of the stomachs of the children, approximately 28 per cent greater than the increase caused by the water meal. After 75 minutes the size of the stomach shadows had reduced somewhat, but they were still almost twice the size of those measured after the water meal. These results explain the satiety and sense of fulness and a submerging of appetite which follow the consumption of candy or sweets. It is worthy of note that this effect may last 90 minutes with a sugar concentration as low as 10 per cent.

A study of gastrointestinal activity is productive of significant observations other than those factors which indicate gastrointestinal response. In metabolic studies gastrointestinal activity must be considered as a possible cause of certain phenomena rather than a result. Practically all recent experimental work on the nutrition and growth of normal children has added emphasis to the necessity of considering the particular individual in interpreting the results obtained with him. Gastric tone and the force of gastric peristalsis may be changed by different stimuli operating in sufficient strengths on the small and large intestines. Little absorption occurs from the stomach, although that organ carries out important digestive functions by means of its mechanical churning actions and its enzyme system. Among the conditions within the intestine that affect gastric motor activity are mechanical distension, chemical irritation, the action of hypertonic or hypotonic solutions, and the presence of products of protein and starch digestion. Studies indicate that the complex carbohydrates may stimulate protein retention and that the character of the fiber may have physiologic importance in the diet. The decomposition or fermentation of the crude fiber in the digestive tract of man is affected by age and the makeup of the plant cell membrane, by the proportion of the components of unavailable carbohydrates, and by the daily mixture as a whole.

Influence of Intestinal Growth

Length of exposure to the various digestive and absorptive processes which occur in the gastrointestinal tract exerts a major influence on the efficiency with which nutriments are assimilated. The most profound changes in the ingesta occur in the small intestine, and it is here that most of the products of digestion are absorbed. Digestion and absorption may continue in the large intestine, where excreted material is added to the residue from digestion. The total length and the extent of surface area of the alimentary tract, therefore, may have significance in the movements and biochemical processes of the digestive tract.

Scammon (1923) summarized early studies on the growth in length of the large and small intestines in man. Table 7 gives the values for childhood which were obtained by interpolating from Scammon's data. During the ages of 4–12 years the small intestine increased 36 per cent, the large intestine 40 per cent, and the total length 36 per cent. The enlarged surface area of the alimentary tract permits a longer time of exposure of the ingesta to digestive processes and a greater surface area through which absorption of nutrients may occur.

In a study of the relationship of length of large intestine to length of small intestine, Scammon observed that, from birth through childhood, the small intestine increased in length at a faster rate than the large intestine, a relationship that remained nearly constant during the ages observed in this study (Table 7). Relationships between the lengths of the body, trunk, and large and small intestines make it possible to determine intestinal growth.

TABLE 7

ESTIMATED LENGTH OF INTESTINAL TRACT IN CHILDREN*

MEASUREMENTS	AVERAGE AGE GROUP		
	4–6 Years	7–9 Years	10–12 Years
Length of intestine:			
Large, cm.	99	112	126
Small, cm.	475	540	618
Total, cm.	574	652	744
Ratios:			
Large/small intestine	1:4.8	1:4.8	1:4.9
Trunk/total intestine	1:14.8	1:15.1	....

* Based on data from Scammon (1923).

Studies of the relationships of length of intestines to number of bowel movements per day, elimination rate, average daily water content, dry weight and fiber content of feces, and average disappearance of the total complex carbohydrates as they progress through the digestive tract indicate that the growth of the intestinal tract is an important factor in meeting nutrient requirements for growth and development. The average number of hours required for the food to pass through the alimentary canal—elimination time—of our children increased with age—19 hours, 30 hours, and 32 hours for the three age groups. At the same time the average number of defecations—laxation rate—decreased from 1.8 to 1.6 to 1.3 per day (Table 8). These trends would be expected, inasmuch as the children grew normally, their food intake increased to meet nutritive and activity requirements, and the length and the absorptive surface of the intestinal tract increased, permitting extended exposure of the food to digestive and assimilative activities and to bacterial action.

TABLE 8

FACTORS RELATING TO GASTROINTESTINAL EXCRETION

FACTORS	AVERAGE AGE GROUP		
	4-6 Years	7-9 Years	10-12 Years
Elimination time, hr.*	19	30	32
Laxation rate†	1.8	1.6	1.3
Fresh weight of feces, gm./day	86	94	108
Per cent of fresh food intake‡ . . .	5.1	5.1	4.7
Dry weight of feces, gm./day	16	18	22
Per cent of dry intake	4.4	4.5	4.5
Per cent of fresh intake	0.94	0.97	0.93
Per cent of fresh feces	18	19	20

* Average time required for carmine marker to traverse tract.
† Average number of defecations per day.
‡ Wet food intake includes drinking water.

EXCRETIONS

Although there is only one normal pathway for food consumption, there are several paths of excretion, namely, the gastrointestinal tract, the kidneys, the skin, and the lungs. The various paths of excretion are closely interrelated, and the well-being of the body as a whole depends on their co-ordinated physiologic functioning.

Gastrointestinal Tract

Unused food residues, waste excretions and secretions, bacteria and their waste products, cell debris, water, and mineral salts egress from the alimentary tract. The consistency and amount of fecal bulk depend on these substances together with the character of the diet, eating habits, water intake, elimination habits, and the individual's physiologic and neurologic pattern. Even when the same foods are consumed in like quantities each day, and elimination habits and hygienic and environmental conditions are standardized, there are daily variations in the performance of the individual's gastrointestinal tract as well as variations among individuals of similar age.

The fundamental processes of growth, including the conversion of food into body tissue, primarily are dependent on adequate digestive functioning. Heredity, body type, posture, change in the position of stomach and other organs, and rapid growth in length of the various segments of the gastrointestinal tract may have considerable significance in the movements and biochemical processes of the alimentary system. As growth proceeds, the gastrointestinal tract must furnish the body with adequate assimilable food material for expanded maintenance and functioning.

Unfortunately, there is no exact procedure for determining when the gastrointestinal pattern has become fully established and to what extent this pattern affects the rate of passage of food through the alimentary tract and the elimination rate at different stages of growth.

Fecal Excretion and Composition

In our effort to acquire a better understanding of the physiology of the gastrointestinal tract and its activity in the normal child during growth, we have determined the rate of passage of food residues through the alimentary tract and the relationship between the fresh and dry weights and the vegetable-fiber contents of food intake and fecal excretion. The results are presented by age groups in Tables 8, 9, and 10.

The elimination time of the children was judged by the number of hours elapsing between the ingestion of a carmine marker and its appearance in the feces. In a special roentgenologic study of carmine accompanied by a barium test meal, it was observed that, although the gastric emptying time was decreased, on the average by 31 per cent, the time required for passage through the tract was unaltered. Therefore, during the regular metabolic-balance studies the carmine was given with a normal breakfast of mixed foods every fifth day. This record of many consecutive markers passing through the tract became a valuable and reliable aid in determining the elimination time. Although the elimination time may vary considerably among different individuals, ranging from 18 to 50 hours, the average elimination time was 27 hours in our subjects. Both the elimination time and the laxation rate assist in expressing gastrointestinal motility.

Although both the fresh and the dry weights of feces showed an increase with age, this increase did not parallel the increase in water intake (see Table 5), indicating that neither the amount nor the consistency of fecal excretion was a result of the water consumed. There was, however, a close relationship between fresh and dry weights of *total* food intake and fresh and dry weights of the feces, as shown by the percentages given in Table 8.

On the basis of increasing age and food consumption, there was an increase in fecal excretion, total solids, fat-free total solids, total nitrogen, fecal energy, and fecal fat (Table 9). Fecal bacteria contribute approximately one-fourth to one-half of the over-all total

TABLE 9

AVERAGE DAILY FECAL COMPOSITION

FECAL COMPONENTS	AVERAGE AGE GROUP		
	4–6 Years	7–9 Years	10–12 Years
Total solids, gm./day............	15.8	18.0	21.6
Fat-free solids, gm./day..........	14.2	15.5	18.1
Fecal excretion:			
Total nitrogen, gm./day........	1.10	1.20	1.34
Energy (heat of combustion),			
Cal./day	75	86	107
Per cent of intake............	4	4	4
Per cent of outgo............	55	53	54
Fecal fat:			
Total, gm./day	1.7	2.4	3.7
Per cent of fresh feces........	2.0	2.5	3.4
Per cent of dry feces	10.8	13.3	17.2

fecal solids and a great deal of the fecal nitrogen and fat (Shohl, 1939). The fecal fat of children may contain some undigested fat from the food, but most of it is derived from bacteria and cellular debris of the alimentary canal and fat excreted into the intestine. Although the actual amount of fecal energy excreted increased with age, the percentages of energy excretion in relation to total intake and total outgo of energy remained approximately constant throughout childhood. The values for fat excretion showed an increase in both fresh and dry feces.

The actual amounts of complex carbohydrates excreted in fecal fiber showed no consistent trend during childhood when determined on the basis of grams per day. When these amounts were considered as a percentage of total solids excreted, however, or as a percentage of total intake, there was a relative decrease (Table 10). The same general observations apply to the energy excreted in fecal fiber. The methods of determination used indicated a wide individual variation among the children in their ability to digest vegetable fibers. The trends by age groups, shown in Table 10, may need to be verified by more refined methods.

The gastrointestinal tract aids in maintaining the electroneutrality of the body by favoring assimilation and secretion of the most needed minerals from the diet. The fecal excretion, therefore, may

TABLE 10

AVERAGE DAILY FECAL FIBER

	AVERAGE AGE GROUP		
FECAL COMPONENTS	4–6 Years	7–9 Years	10–12 Years
Fecal complex carbohydrates:			
Total, gm./day	3.10	3.17	2.58
Per cent of total solids	20	18	12
Per cent of intake	52	50	37
Energy (heat of combustion):*			
Total, Cal./day	13	13	10
Per cent of fecal energy	17	15	10
Cellulose, gm./day	0.50	0.64	0.64
Hemicellulose, gm./day	0.77	0.93	0.64
Lignin, gm./day	1.83	1.60	1.30

* Factor for CHO, 4.1.

contain nutrient materials which have been discarded by reason of the body's selective action, in addition to some food materials that have remained undigested, as well as intestinal secretions and excretions. Table 11 shows that calcium, magnesium, potassium, and phosphorus compose the greater part of the minerals excreted in the feces. Relatively small quantities of sodium, sulfur, and chlorine are eliminated by this metabolic route. The electropositive and electronegative minerals, together, compose approximately 10 per cent of the total weight of the fecal solids; an average of about 6 per cent of the total weight of the fecal solids consists of the positive minerals. The total positive and negative minerals found in the fecal excretion form about 0.4 per cent of the total dry weight of the dietary intake. Table 12 gives the average daily amounts and percent-

TABLE 11

AVERAGE DAILY MINERAL COMPOSITION OF FECES

FECAL MINERALS	AVERAGE AGE GROUP		
	4–6 Years	7–9 Years	10–12 Years
Electropositive minerals:			
Calcium, mg./day	496	713	684
Per cent of intake	61	75	65
Magnesium, mg./day	167	174	180
Per cent of intake	58	58	56
Sodium, mg./day	40	33	34
Per cent of intake	2	1	1
Potassium, mg./day	307	373	420
Per cent of intake	12	13	12
Electronegative minerals:			
Phosphorus, mg./day	312	445	488
Per cent of intake	28	34	30
Chlorine, mg./day	56	52	37
Per cent of intake	2	1	1
Sulfur, mg./day	81	97	129
Per cent of intake	12	12	13

TABLE 12

AVERAGE DAILY FECAL POSITIVE AND NEGATIVE MINERALS

FECAL MINERALS	AVERAGE AGE GROUP		
	4–6 Years	7–9 Years	10–12 Years
Electropositive minerals:			
Total, gm./day	1.0	1.3	1.3
Per cent of intake	17	20	17
Per cent of total outgo	20	22	19
Total, meq./day	48	61	61
Per cent of intake	22	24	20
Per cent of total outgo	25	27	24
Electronegative minerals:			
Total, gm./day	0.4	0.6	0.7
Per cent of intake	9	10	9
Per cent of total outgo	10	11	10
Total, meq./day	25	34	37
Per cent of intake	12	15	13
Per cent of total outgo	14	16	15
Positive plus negative minerals:			
Total, gm./day	1.4	1.9	2.0
Total, meq./day	73	95	98

ages of positive and negative minerals in the feces, in terms of intake and total outgo, for the three age groups of childhood.

Urinary Excretion and Composition

Urine is eliminated at intervals but is excreted continuously by the kidneys and collected in the urinary bladder. It is composed of approximately 95 per cent water and contains solids which have their origin in the surpluses of the intake and in the waste products of metabolism. The composition of urine varies widely, depending on the amount and kind of food consumed, water intake, environ-

TABLE 13

AVERAGE DAILY URINARY COMPOSITION

URINARY COMPONENTS	AVERAGE AGE GROUP		
	4–6 Years	7–9 Years	10–12 Years
Total solids, gm./day..........	32.8	38.4	46.1
Nitrogen:			
Total, gm./day..............	7.93	9.62	10.88
Per cent of intake.........	81	85	83
Per cent of outgo..........	88	89	89
Energy (heat of combustion):			
Total, Cal./day.............	62	76	92
Per cent of intake.........	3	4	4
Per cent of outgo.........	45	47	46

ment, and intensity of the physiologic activity involved in the maintenance of the osmotic and ionic equilibriums of the body. The nitrogenous constituents discharged are primarily end products of protein metabolism. The minerals excreted are derived from the food ingested and from the metabolic processes concerned in growth and in the maintenance of the electroneutrality of the body.

For the children in our study the mean daily urine volume was 770 ml. The mean specific gravity was 1.024. The average daily urinary total solids, nitrogen, and energy are presented in Table 13. Excretion of all three components increased with age, as did the total food intake.

Although the dietary intake for each child remained similar in composition, the amounts of positive and negative minerals excreted varied from day to day, depending on current metabolic demands for maintenance, growth, and development. Sodium, potassium, and chlorine were excreted in greatest quantities (Table 14) and in increasing amounts with age and food consumed. The average daily urinary excretion of total electropositive and electronegative minerals is presented in Table 15.

TABLE 14

AVERAGE DAILY MINERAL COMPOSITION OF URINE

URINARY MINERALS	AVERAGE AGE GROUP		
	4–6 Years	7–9 Years	10–12 Years
Electropositive minerals:			
Calcium, mg./day............	118	102	110
Per cent of intake.........	15	11	10
Magnesium, mg./day........	74	85	100
Per cent of intake.........	26	29	31
Sodium, mg./day............	1,835	2,194	2,560
Per cent of intake.........	86	90	85
Potassium, mg./day.........	2,038	2,263	2,775
Per cent of intake.........	79	78	80
Electronegative minerals:			
Phosphorus, mg./day........	658	716	871
Per cent of intake.........	59	56	55
Chlorine, mg./day...........	2,978	3,463	3,988
Per cent of intake.........	88	93	91
Sulfur, mg./day.............	532	648	749
Per cent of intake.........	78	83	74

Water Exchange

The movement of water into and out of the body is an important factor in maintaining homeostasis of the body and its tissues. In growth, water is utilized in the construction of new protoplasmic tissue and its concomitant enlarged function.

Our subjects ingested an average of 1,541 gm. of water per day, inclusive of moisture of food, and acquired an additional 239 gm. of water per day formed during the metabolism of foodstuffs in the body, making the total average amount of water available daily 1,780 gm. Of this amount, 750 gm. was eliminated through the kidneys and 78 gm. in the feces, leaving 952 gm. which must have been used otherwise by the body, that is, lost through evaporation from the skin and lungs or incorporated into body tissue. If the body is considered as two-thirds water, the average daily weight gain of the children, 7.1 gm. would represent an average of 5 gm. of water retained per day for use in fabrication and function of new protoplasmic tissue.

TABLE 15

AVERAGE DAILY URINARY POSITIVE AND NEGATIVE MINERALS

URINARY COMPONENTS	AVERAGE AGE GROUP		
	4–6 Years	7–9 Years	10–12 Years
Electropositive minerals:			
Total, gm./day..............	4.1	4.7	5.6
Per cent of intake.........	70	70	70
Per cent of outgo..........	80	78	81
Total, meq./day.............	144	165	196
Per cent of intake.........	65	66	66
Per cent of outgo..........	75	73	76
Electronegative minerals:			
Total, gm./day..............	4.2	4.8	5.6
Per cent of intake.........	80	83	80
Per cent of outgo.........	90	89	90
Total, meq./day.............	155	180	210
Per cent of intake.........	77	78	75
Per cent of outgo.........	86	84	85
Positive plus negative minerals:			
Total, gm./day..............	8.3	9.5	11.2
Total, meq./day.............	299	345	406

Skin Excretion and Lung Ventilation

DuBois (1936, 1937) observed 12-year-old boys under standard conditions and found that they lost an average of 27 per cent of their energy through evaporation of water. In our study of growth the average energy loss for childhood was 3.7 and 4.2 per cent through the urine and feces, respectively, totaling 7.9 per cent, an amount very close to Rubner's 8–10 per cent (Lusk, 1928). Subtracting the heat of combustion of urine and feces from that of the food intake provides an estimate of the physiologic fuel value of the diet to the individuals studied, that is, the energy, or heat of combustion, which has been derived from food, expended in the conduct of the physiologic activities, and laid down in body tissues. The physiologic fuel value represents approximately 92 per cent of the heat of combustion energy of the food consumed, as shown in Table 16.

It was assumed that our children were physiologically similar to those observed by DuBois, losing an average of 27 per cent of their energy intake through vaporization of water from the skin and lungs, and that they were active to approximately the same degree. The total daily energy dissipated averaged 487, 554, and 660 Cal. for the three age groups on the basis of heat of combus-

TABLE 16

AVERAGE DAILY ENERGY EXCHANGE

ENERGY	AVERAGE AGE GROUP		
	4–6 Years	7–9 Years	10–12 Years
Energy (heat of combustion):			
Intake, Cal./day	1,803	2,051	2,443
Urine plus feces:			
Total, Cal./day	137	162	199
Per cent of intake	7	8	8
Estimated loss via skin and lungs:			
Total, Cal./day*	487	554	660
Total, water loss, gm./day†	840	955	1,138
Physiological fuel value:			
Intake, Cal./day	1,666	1,889	2,244
Per cent of intake (heat of combustion)	93	92	92
Estimated loss via skin and lungs:			
Total, Cal./day*	450	510	606
Total water loss, gm./day†	776	879	1,045

* 27 per cent of total calories of children lost by evaporation of water from skin and lungs (DuBois, 1936, 1937).

† 0.58 Cal. is required to vaporize each gram of water from the surface of the body at room temperature.

tion of food intake and 450, 510, and 606 Cal. on the basis of physiologic fuel value—determined heat of food intake minus urine and feces. Under conditions of normal activity and living, the adult displays a tendency to rid himself, by evaporation of water, of about one-fourth of the heat produced within his body. Children appear to dissipate daily a greater amount of energy than adults, an observation which is in line with greater activity and enhanced metabolism due to the physiologic processes of growth.

It has been observed that 0.58 Cal. is required to vaporize each gram of water from the surface of the body at room temperature. When this value of heat of vaporization of water was applied to the three age groups in our study, it was found that they excreted daily approximately 840, 955, and 1,138 gm. of water on the basis of determined heat of the food intake and 776, 879, and 1,045 gm. on the basis of physiologic fuel value. These figures are surprisingly close to the estimated daily insensible water loss of 746, 942, and 1,167 ml. for the respective average age groups based on the value of 1,000 ml. of water per square meter per 24 hours which Heeley and Talbot (1955) considered reasonable to cover the insensible losses of the ordinary child, whose neurohypophyseal-renal homeostatic system is functionally adequate. Although the results of calculations such as the foregoing may be considered only as broad approximations, they indicate that children dispose of a greater amount of water daily than the 600–700 gm. which has been estimated for an adult man.

As water is eliminated through the skin, it carries with it appreciable amounts of sodium, potassium, and chlorine, those elements most concerned with water metabolism. Skin-excretion determinations are exceedingly difficult to ascertain. For this reason the calculated retentions of sodium, potassium, chlorine, and sulfur from analyses of food intake and outgo may be considerably higher than the actual amounts of these elements retained.

NUTRIENT ABSORPTION

Since most food materials ingested must be broken down into smaller molecules before nutritionally significant quantities of nutrients may be absorbed, there exists in the gastrointestinal tract an effective enzymatic system for hydrolyzing and preparing the ingesta for absorption into the body. Only small amounts of nutrients are absorbed into the blood stream by way of the gastric mucosa. By far the greatest absorption takes place in the small intestine. This is due to the great length of the small intestine and its specifically adapted mucosa with its enlarged surface of the villi in the epithelial lining. As the nutrients pass through the intestinal mucosa into the blood stream, they may be prepared further for absorption and utilization by the cells of the body.

Absorbed nutrients may leave the small intestine by two routes: by way of the blood capillaries in the walls of the small intestine or by way of the lymph system. In the former pathway the nutrients absorbed in the blood capillaries pass to the mesenteric veins and the portal vein and then through the liver and into the general circulation. The liver, which is enlarging during childhood, transforms the chemical structure of many of the absorbed nutrients in preparation for their utilization in other tissues of the body. Those food elements that are absorbed by way of the lymph vessels in the small intestine and the lacteals pass into the thoracic duct and then into the venous blood system.

The average daily nutrient absorption of children has been obtained by subtracting the fecal excretion from the food intake. Table 17 presents the observed average daily absorption by age groups. In our experimental studies we found that the diet most favorable for utilization of nutrients (see Fig. 1) and, therefore, for meeting the requirements of chemical growth and development was composed of approximately 35 per cent vegetable protein and 65 per cent animal protein. It has an energy-content distribution of about 15 per cent protein, 41 per cent fat, and 44 per cent carbohydrate and an alkaline ash value ranging from 0.48 to 1.11 milliequivalents (meq.) per kilogram per day. Of the foodstuffs consumed by the children, approximately 89 per cent of the protein, 97 per cent of the carbohydrate, and 97 per cent of the fat were absorbed into the general blood circulation. On the basis of the three age groups indicated, about 72.5 gm., 67.5 gm., and 62.5 gm. of protein were absorbed per square meter of surface area, or 2.9 gm., 2.6 gm., and 2.2 gm. per kilogram of body weight. Figure 2 shows the actual distribution and Figure 3 the relative distribution of food intake for our subjects.

It was found that on the average 33 per cent of their calcium intake was absorbed, or approximately 327 mg. per square meter of surface area, or 12 mg. per kilogram. Ninety-nine per cent of the sodium and chlorine, 88 per cent of the potassium and sulfur, 42 per cent of the magnesium, and 69 per cent of the phosphorus intake were absorbed. Of the total positive minerals—calcium, magnesium, sodium, and potassium—78 per cent was absorbed; of the total negative minerals—phosphorus, chlorine, and sulfur—87 per cent. The complex carbohydrates were broken down in the digestive tract to the extent that 76 per cent of the cellulose and 74 per cent of the hemicellulose were absorbed.

TABLE 17

AVERAGE DAILY NUTRIENT ABSORPTION

NUTRIENT ABSORBED	4–6 Years				7–9 Years				10–12 Years			
	Total	Per Cent of Intake	Per Kg.	Per Sq. M.	Total	Per Cent of Intake	Per Kg.	Per Sq. M.	Total	Per Cent of Intake	Per Kg.	Per Sq. M.
Nitrogen, gm.	8.69	89	0.47	11.6	10.12	89	0.41	10.8	11.81	90	0.35	10.0
Protein (N×6.25), gm.	54.3	89	2.9	72.5	63.2	89	2.6	67.5	73.8	90	2.2	62.5
Carbohydrate, gm.	187	97			204	98			228	97		
Fat, gm.	69.0	98	3.8		81.4	97	3.4		103.6	97	3.1	
Calcium, mg.	311	39	16	414	234	25	9	248	375	35	11	320
Calcium, meq.	15		0.8	21	12		0.5	12	19		0.6	16
Magnesium, mg.	119	42	6.4	160	125	42	5.1	132	144	44	4.2	123
Magnesium, meq.	10		0.5	13	10		0.4	11	12		0.3	10
Sodium, mg.	2,089	98	113	2,798	2,403	99	97	2,542	2,970	99	88	2,527
Sodium, meq.	91		4.9	122	105		4.2	111	129		3.8	110
Potassium, mg.	2,275	88	124	3,055	2,515	87	102	2,660	3,066	88	90	2,604
Potassium, meq.	58		3.2	78	64		2.6	68	78		2.3	67
Phosphorus, mg.	802	72	43	1,074	840	66	34	884	1,104	70	32	940
Phosphorus, meq.	47		2.5	62	49		2.0	51	64		1.9	55
Chlorine, mg.	3,314	98	179	4,441	3,699	99	150	3,926	4,359	99	128	3,711
Chlorine, meq.	93		5.1	125	104		4.2	111	123		3.6	104
Sulfur, mg.	600	88	32	804	689	88	28	730	880	87	26	749
Sulfur, meq.	37		2.0	50	43		1.7	46	55		1.6	47
Total minerals:												
Positive, meq.	174	78	9.4	234	191	76	7.7	202	238	80	7.0	203
Negative, meq.	177	88	9.6	237	196	85	7.9	208	242	87	7.1	206

The column headers "4–6 Years", "7–9 Years", "10–12 Years" fall under the spanning heading AVERAGE AGE GROUP.

61

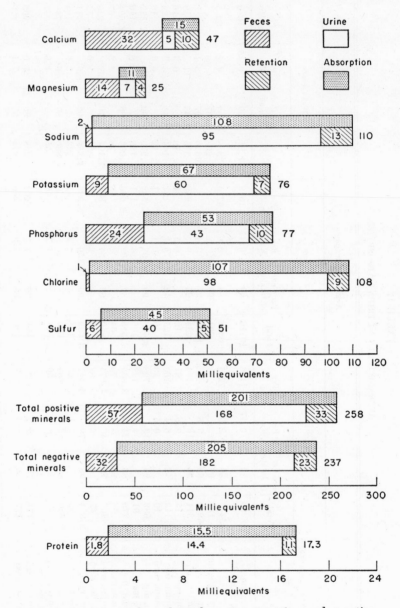

Fɪɢ. 2.—Nutrient intake and its absorption, retention, and excretion

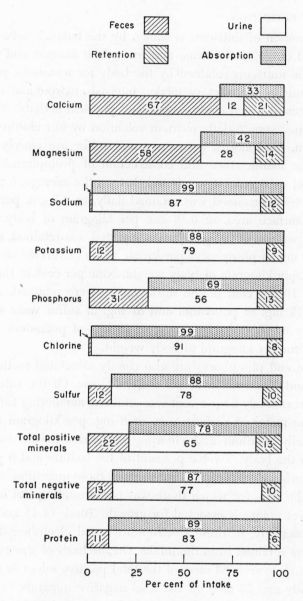

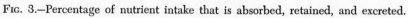

FIG. 3.—Percentage of nutrient intake that is absorbed, retained, and excreted.

NUTRIENT RETENTION

The retention of nutrients is shown by the balance between the intake and outgo in the urine and feces. The amount and proportions of the nutrients retained by the body for metabolic purposes will depend on age, dietary intake, internal environment and nutritive status, external environment, and physical activity. Table 18 presents the average daily nutrient retention by our children.

Nitrogen, phosphorus, potassium, and sulfur are closely associated in the maintenance and construction of protoplasmic tissue. For boys of 4–12 years it was found that, on the average, 6 per cent of the protein consumed was retained daily, or 4.8 gm. per square meter of surface area, or 0.18 gm. per kilogram of body weight. About 13 per cent of the phosphorus ingested was retained, amounting to 176 mg. of phosphorus per square meter of surface area daily, or 6.5 mg. per kilogram of body weight. Nine per cent of the potassium and 10 per cent of the sulfur intake were retained. Approximately 277 mg. of potassium and 81 mg. of sulfur were retained per square meter of surface area, or 10 mg. of potassium and 2.9 mg. of sulfur per kilogram of body weight.

Calcium and phosphorus are also closely associated in the maintenance and construction of the skeletal tissue. Of the calcium intake, approximately 21 per cent was retained, amounting to 209 mg. per square meter of surface area, or 8 mg. per kilogram of body weight daily. Sodium and chlorine participate in the water exchange in the body. Twelve per cent of the sodium and 8 per cent of the chlorine were retained, but some of these quantities were lost through the skin, for which there was no accounting. An excess of cations over anions is essential for growth. Totals of 13 and 10 per cent, respectively, of these electropositive and electronegative elements were retained from the intake. On the basis of square meters of body surface area, 34 meq. of the total positive minerals were retained daily and 25 meq. of the total negative minerals, or, on the basis of per kilogram of body weight, 1.28 meq. and 0.92 meq.

TABLE 18

AVERAGE DAILY NUTRIENT RETENTION

NUTRIENT RETAINED	AVERAGE AGE GROUP											
	4–6 Years				7–9 Years				10–12 Years			
	Total	Per Cent of Intake	Per Kg.	Per Sq. M.	Total	Per Cent of Intake	Per Kg.	Per Sq. M.	Total	Per Cent of Intake	Per Kg.	Per Sq. M.
Nitrogen, gm.	0.76	8	0.040	1.00	0.50	4	0.020	0.53	0.93	7	0.028	0.80
Protein (N×6.25), gm.	4.8	8	0.25	6.2	3.1	4	0.12	3.3	5.8	7	0.18	5.0
Calcium, mg.	193	24	10.2	256	132	14	5.5	144	265	25	7.7	227
Calcium, meq.	9.7		0.51	12.8	6.6		0.28	7.2	13.2		0.38	11.4
Magnesium, mg.	45	16	2.4	60	40	13	1.6	43	44	13	1.3	38
Magnesium, meq.	3.7		0.20	4.9	3.3		0.13	3.5	3.6		0.11	3.1
Sodium, mg.	254	12	13.3	336	209	9	8.2	218	410	14	11.9	348
Sodium, meq.	11.0		0.58	14.6	9.1		0.36	9.5	17.8		0.52	15.2
Potassium, mg.	237	9	11.3	317	252	9	10.2	266	291	8	8.6	247
Potassium, meq.	6.0		0.29	8.1	6.5		0.26	6.8	7.4		0.22	6.3
Phosphorus, mg.	144	13	7.5	190	124	10	5.2	135	233	15	6.8	202
Phosphorus, meq.	8.3		0.44	11.0	7.2		0.30	7.9	13.5		0.40	11.7
Chlorine, mg.	336	10	18.0	449	236	6	9.4	248	371	8	10.8	314
Chlorine, meq.	9.5		0.51	12.7	6.6		0.27	7.0	10.4		0.30	8.9
Sulfur, mg.	68	10	3.4	89	41	5	1.6	42	131	13	3.8	113
Sulfur, meq.	4.2		0.21	5.5	2.6		0.10	2.6	8.2		0.24	7.0
Total minerals:												
Positive, meq.	30.4	13	1.58	40.4	25.5	10	1.03	27.0	42.0	14	1.23	36.0
Negative, meq.	22.0	11	1.16	29.2	16.4	7	0.67	17.5	32.1	12	0.94	27.6

SIGNIFICANCE OF METABOLIC FATE OF NUTRIENTS
TO GROWTH AND DEVELOPMENT

The development and maintenance of healthy body structure depend on the supply of many food substances and the fate of the nutrients therein as they proceed through the metabolic processes of digestion, absorption, and excretion or utilization. There must be sufficient energy present in the food intake to meet the needs of activity and the maintenance of body temperature and basal heat production and to permit full utilization of the essential amino acids for the synthesis of protoplasmic tissue in fulfilment of immediate growth and developmental needs. If the diet does not provide enough energy, the protein intake cannot be fully utilized. Furthermore, the protein of the body tissues may be sacrificed and burned as fuel to provide for activity requirements.

Consideration must be given to the kinds and amounts of fat in the diet, to deficiencies or excesses of different minerals, and to the presence of vitamins to regulate enzyme and functional activities in the body. On the fate of the metabolites will depend the maintenance of homeostatic and functional equilibriums while growth and development take place. The concentrations and proportions of nutrients and metabolites found in the excretions of urine, feces, and skin give significant information on the type of growth and nutrition that is occurring.

The cation and anion contents of the urine result from the body's effort to maintain the fluids and tissues at the physiologically proper hydrogen-ion concentration that is essential for life. There are numerous factors that may enter into the adjustment or control of the acidity and alkalinity of urine, which result from the type of diet consumed and the physiologic processes accompanying its digestion, absorption, and utilization. The total amount of any one component excreted during a 24-hour period depends on the child's characteristic physiologic makeup and growth demands, the diet, and the environment.

CHAPTER FIVE

Body Composition

*Macro biochemical and functional analyses preserve and enhance
the picture of the individual as a whole even though the mosaic pattern of component parts is delineated at the same time quantitatively.*

BEHNKE (1953*b*)

Assessment of the chemical composition of the body and the composition of the gain or loss in body weight during growth and
maturation are major objectives in the present study of childhood.
Because of the dynamic character of the body, its composition is
subject to constant fluctuation. This results from the varying rates at
which the individual organs grow and mature. This variability is
clearly demonstrated by Scammon's four types of growth curves—
general, neural, lymphoid, and genital. The greatest change during
childhood occurs in the lymphoid type. The least change occurs in
the genital type. The change in the other two types is about equal.
The metabolism of the individual organs varies with their stage of
maturity.

Very few direct chemical analyses of human bodies or even parts
of bodies have been recorded. The problems of obtaining suitable
bodies and of analyzing them accurately are almost insurmountable.
In most instances the bodies available for autopsy have not been of
healthy individuals, and the data obtained do not represent normal
body composition values. More fetuses have been subjected to analysis than bodies of infants, children, or adults. Widdowson *et al.*
(1951) analyzed the major chemical components of the body of a
male child 4½ years old with a body weight of 14 kg. and a height
of 107 cm. Although the analyses are of great value, these investigators point out that the data must be interpreted with great caution
and that many more bodies will have to be analyzed before reliable
figures for the normal average and its variations can be established.

In their studies of the chemical composition of body tissues of animals, Moulton (1923) and Hastings (1940–41) emphasized the importance of a quantitative evaluation of body weight with specific reference to fat, fat-free tissue mass, water, and minerals. Moulton observed that the concentration of water, protein, and ash of the fat-free mass becomes more or less stationary, a state he called "chemical maturity." Applying his results to human beings, he surmised that by early childhood the fat-free protoplasmic mass has reached a fairly constant chemical composition. This theory is supported by our chemical studies, as well as the investigations of other workers, which indicate that growth and development are most uniform between the ages of 4 and 9 years.

In later systematic work involving detailed analyses of whole bodies of several species of mammals including man at various ages, Spray and Widdowson (1950) pointed out that mammals similar morphologically have similar composition and that the term "chemical maturity" can be applied to the body as a whole only when all its constituents have reached constant level. In a recent report on continuing studies of linear growth of long bones (Maresh, 1955), it is stated:

Beginning at about three or four years of age and continuing to the prepubescent years, the childhood patterns of long-bone growth were found to be remarkably stable and orderly. Here the changes in percentile levels with increasing age were minimal, fluctuations were few, and the growth curves for all four bones (humerus, radius, femur, and tibia) were usually alike descriptively. "Latency" would seem to be a good term for linear physical growth in the childhood years.

During World War II intensive research on body composition was stimulated, and new methods were developed for *in vivo* chemical analysis of the human body. Under the leadership of Behnke (1941–42), practical procedures were developed for partitioning the body weight of living adults into its major components. The results have been extended and verified in principle by other investigators, and they agree, in general, with the few data obtained by direct chemical analysis of adult human bodies. We have since adapted these standard values for the purpose of calculating the distribution of the body weight of children into its component parts—total body water, extracellular water, intracellular water, lean body mass, and fat (Macy and Kelly, 1956). Thus it is possible to predict with reasonable accuracy body composition in childhood in relation to physical and chemical growth and maturation. Some of the tests previously described were taken into consideration: anthropometric measurements, roentgenographic assessments, and biochemical studies of urine and basal oxygen consumption and gastrointestinal rate. The fact that so many independent evaluations were made, both direct and indirect, provided a check on the methods used and the values obtained.

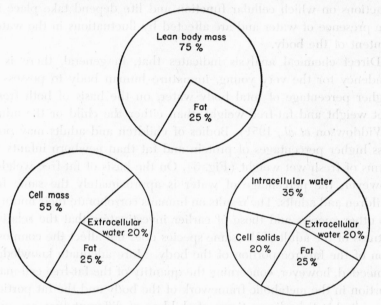

Fig. 4.—Estimated body composition *in vivo* of boys

TERMINOLOGY

Investigators studying body composition have used various terms for components of body weight. Body composition (Fig. 4) consists of lean body mass and fat. Lean body mass, in turn, can be divided into cell solids, extracellular water, and intracellular water. Intracellular water and cell solids combined give cell mass.

Some adjustments have been made in our calculations to correct for differences in terminology. Lean body mass, as used in our evaluations, includes no fat. In Behnke's definition (1941–42) of this term a certain amount of "essential" fat is assumed. Therefore, when Behnke's equations were applied, his values were adjusted to eliminate the 10 per cent essential fat for boys and the 15 per cent for girls that he had included in lean body mass. We have included this "essential" fat in total body fat, which makes our values for total fat appear higher than those reported by Behnke.

BODY-WATER EVALUATION

Water is essential for the construction, function, and maintenance of the homeostatic condition of the body. The physicochemical reactions on which cellular function and life depend take place in the presence of water and are affected by fluctuations in the water content of the body.

Direct chemical analysis indicates that, in general, there is a tendency for the very young, immature human body to possess a higher percentage of total body water, on the basis of both fresh wet weight and fat-free weight, than either the child or the adult (Widdowson *et al.*, 1951). Bodies of children and adults may possess higher percentages of protein and fat than newborn infants in terms of fresh wet weight (Fig. 5). On the basis of fat-free weight, however, the percentage of water is approximately the same for children and adults. The results on humans corroborate their findings on other species and those of earlier investigators that the relative fatness of the adult of the same species does not affect the composition of the fat-free portion of the body. More adequate knowledge is needed, however, concerning the quantity of the fat-free cell-mass portion in the metabolic framework of the body and the fat portion deposited in the adipose tissue of children of different ages, sex, and activities.

Three methods have been employed in the measurement of the volume of water in the body:

1. Chemical analysis by the desiccation procedure applied after death (Mitchell, 1944; McCance and Widdowson, 1951; Widdowson *et al.*, 1951; Forbes *et al.*, 1953)
2. *In vivo* dilution procedures employing a variety of chemical substances (Morse *et al.*, 1947; Pace *et al.*, 1947; Soberman, 1949; Osserman *et al.*, 1950; Steele *et al.*, 1950; Kraybill *et al.*, 1951; Widdowson *et al.*, 1951; Miller and Blyth, 1952)
3. The method of water displacement for determining specific gravity of living persons and cadavers (Zook, 1932; Boyd, 1933; Behnke *et al.*, 1942; Messinger and Steele, 1949; Keys *et al.*, 1950)

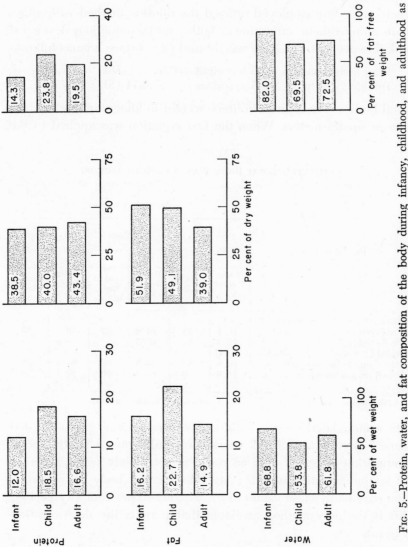

Fig. 5.—Protein, water, and fat composition of the body during infancy, childhood, and adulthood as adapted from the data of Widdowson *et al.* (1951).

The equations derived by Friis-Hansen *et al.* (1951) for determining the volume of total body water of children were directly applicable to the assay of the body composition of our children. Their procedure employed utilized the dilution method with either deuterium oxide or antipyrine or both, and the equations developed took into account (1) body weight and (2) surface area as follows:

Total body water = 0.55 × weight + 0.51   (SD = ±7.4%),
Total body water = 15.05 × surface area − 0.71 (SD = ±7.1%).

Total body water is given in liters, weight in kilograms, and surface area in square meters. When the first equation was applied to the

TABLE 19

ESTIMATED TOTAL BODY WATER IN BODY WEIGHT

PROCEDURE USED	AVERAGE AGE GROUP					
	4–6 Years		7–9 Years		10–12 Years	
	Water Weight (Kg.)	Per Cent of Body Weight	Water Weight (Kg.)	Per Cent of Body Weight	Water Weight (Kg.)	Per Cent of Body Weight
Derived from studies on children:[*]						
Predicted from body weight....	10.7	58	14.2	57	19.3	56
Predicted from surface area....	10.5	57	13.5	54	16.8	49
Adapted from studies on adults:[†]						
Based on chronologic age......	10.8	59	14.9	60	20.1	59
Based on anatomic age........	11.0	59	14.9	60	20.1	59

[*] Friis-Hansen *et al.* (1951).   [†] McCance and Widdowson (1951).

data accumulated on our children, in average age groups of 4–6 years, 7–9 years, and 10–12 years, the results gave a relative body composition of 58, 57, and 56 per cent total body water, whereas the second equation, which takes into account body surface area, gave reasonably close values of 57, 54, and 49 per cent (Table 19). This is the only method available that permits the determination of trends.

Another equation, developed from an independent biochemical procedure by McCance and Widdowson (1951), was also applied to the data gathered on our children:

% total body water = % extracellular water + 67% cell mass.

The prediction equations for estimating the amounts of water, cell mass, and fat in adults, formulated by the method of least squares from data given by these investigators, utilize percentage standard body weight instead of actual body weight. The adaptation of the prediction equations to our children was based on the assumption that the body composition of the average child is the same as for the average adult. In adjusting the McCance and Widdowson data to children, the normal weight values incorporated were those developed by Helen Pryor (1943). These norms were arrived at by use of several physical measurements, namely, sex, age, height, hip breadth, and chest breadth. The prediction equations used in calculating values for our children were as follows:

$$\% \text{ extracellular water} = \frac{-16 \times \text{Observed body weight}}{\text{Standard weight}} + 36.64,$$

$$\% \text{ cell mass} = \frac{-16 \times \text{Observed body weight}}{\text{Standard weight}} + 72.69.$$

Normal weight was estimated by both chronologic and anatomic age. When measurements of body size or composition are based on age, anatomic or skeletal age often gives a truer evaluation. For this reason the percentages of total body water are presented for both chronologic and skeletal age (Table 19). The results obtained for total water amounted to 59, 60, and 59 per cent of the body weight for the three age groups and were comparable to the values derived from the equations of Friis-Hansen *et al.* (1951).

Edelman *et al.* (1952) determined total body water in normal human beings of both sexes throughout the life-span, using the deuterium oxide dilution technique. One hundred and twenty measurements were made on subjects 2 days to 86 years of age with a weight range of from 2.3 to 100.3 kg. No appreciable difference attributable to sex was noted until the age of 16 years; thereafter the mean body water was lower in the females studied than in the males of corresponding age. The ranges of total body water given were 55.2–62.8 per cent of body weight for all subjects from 1 to 9 years, 51.8–63.2 per cent for males from 10 to 16 years, and 49.8–59.5 per cent for females from 10 to 16 years of age.

The estimates of body water given in Table 19 fall within the range found by Edelman *et al.* for normal childhood. Further con-

firmation is thus given to the estimated total body-water values
obtained in our study of nutrition and chemical growth in childhood, inasmuch as the volumes of water compare favorably with
the results obtained by direct chemical analysis by desiccation of
the cadaver of a 4½-year-old child (Widdowson *et al.*, 1951). The
percentage of water in the whole body of the child on a fresh
weight basis amounted to 53.8, which was somewhat lower than the
average for childhood determined in our studies, no doubt because
the child had been ill for two weeks prior to death and its body
water had been reduced some by dehydration (see Fig. 5).

Extracellular Water

Manery (1954) described extracellular fluid as "an ill-defined
physiological unit made up of plasma, lymph, cavity extracellular
fluids and interstitial fluid of tissues. Each type resembles the
plasma in a general way but each one is dissimilar to the plasma
and to all others, in a fashion depending upon the site and function
of the particular tissue of which it is a part." He also distinguished
anatomic and physiologic measurements of extracellular water.

Morse *et al.* (1947) studied 65 normal healthy children, aged
3–17 years, and determined their available fluid volume by the
sodium thiocyanate dilution method. The statistical method of least
squares was used for obtaining the linear equations that best fit the
data, and the following equations were obtained:

For children with surface areas of 0.5–1.2 square meters:

Available fluid volume $= -6.14 + 0.1042$ height (cm.)

Available fluid volume $= -1.48 + 9.12$ surface area (sq. m.)

For children with surface areas of 1.0–2.0 square meters:

Available fluid volume $= -27.20 + 0.2557$ height (cm.)

Available fluid volume $= - 7.15 + 14.22$ surface area (sq. m.)

For the whole range of childhood and adolescence:

Available fluid volume $= - 0.03 + 0.287$ weight (kg.)

On the assumption that the available fluid volume may be considered equivalent to extracellular fluid, we applied these equations
to the data on our children. When the results obtained on the basis
of height, weight, and surface area were averaged for the three age

groups, 28, 29, and 27 per cent of the body weight was estimated to be extracellular water (Table 20).

McCance and Widdowson (1951) developed a simplified method of obtaining body composition which is applicable to living persons. According to their thesis, the body is, in large measure, composed of total body water, extracellular water, cell mass, fat, and minerals. They determined body water by the dilution procedure. In the extracellular fluid determination sodium thiocyanate was used and corrections were made for its penetration into the erythrocytes. The

TABLE 20

ESTIMATED EXTRACELLULAR AND INTRACELLULAR WATER IN BODY WEIGHT

PROCEDURE USED	AVERAGE AGE GROUP					
	4–6 Years		7–9 Years		10–12 Years	
	Water Weight (Kg.)	Per Cent of Body Weight	Water Weight (Kg.)	Per Cent of Body Weight	Water Weight (Kg.)	Per Cent of Body Weight
Extracellular Water:						
Derived from studies on children:						
Predicted from height, weight, and surface area*	5.3	28	7.1	29	9.2	27
Predicted from weight and surface area†	3.0	16	3.9	16	5.1	15
Predicted from weight and surface area‡	3.9	21	5.1	21	6.6	19
Adapted from studies on adults:§						
Based on chronologic age	3.8	21	5.3	21	7.1	21
Based on anatomic age	3.9	21	5.3	21	7.1	21
Intracellular Water:						
Derived from studies on children:						
Predicted from weight and surface area†	7.6	41	9.9	40	12.9	38
Predicted from weight and surface area‡	6.7	36	8.7	35	11.4	34
Adapted from studies on adults:§						
Based on chronologic age	7.0	38	9.6	39	13.0	38
Based on anatomic age	7.1	38	9.6	39	13.0	38

* Morse *et al.* (1947).
† Friis-Hansen *et al.* (1951); Gamble (1947).
‡ Friis-Hansen *et al.* (1951); McCance and Widdowson (1951).
§ McCance and Widdowson (1951).

prediction equation for evaluating the volume of extracellular water in the body, as given above, was derived from the data of McCance and Widdowson by the method of least squares.

The relative amounts of extracellular water of the body as evaluated on the basis of chronologic and anatomic ages are shown in Table 20. The extracelular water was found to occupy 21 per cent of the body weight on the basis of both chronologic and anatomic age.

The relative volumes of extracellular water determined by the prediction equation developed from McCance and Widdowson's data on adult men and women gave lower levels than those obtained by the equation of Morse *et al.* These differences could be accounted for by the possibility that Morse *et al.* made no correction for the penetration of the sodium thiocyanate into the erythrocytes; or the discrepancies may have originated in the application of equations derived for adults to measurements of extracellular fluid in children.

Intracellular Water

McCance and Widdowson measured the amount of cell mass and extracellular water and, assuming that the cells contained 67 per cent by weight of water, calculated the intracellular water. Their average summary value of 59 per cent for total body water and 21 per cent for extracellular water gave an average value for intracellular water of 38 per cent of the body weight in childhood (Table 20).

BODY-FAT EVALUATION

In a review of the general subject of the estimation of fat in the body, Brožek and Keys (1950) state:

While the present orientation is toward nutritional application, it should be observed that estimation of the proportion of fat in the human body is needed for an intelligent interpretation of body weight and its change in different physiological conditions; for the investigation of differential rates of growth and involution of body tissues during the life cycle; for a quantitative description of the physical constitution and "body type," especially with reference to morbidity and mortality trends; and for the study of sex and race differences.

Direct measurements of specific gravity of children (Zook, 1932; Boyd, 1933) and adult men (Behnke, 1941–42; Messinger and Steele, 1949; Keys *et al.*, 1950; Osserman *et al.*, 1950) by the water-displacement method have been used to indicate the fat content of the body.

Determinations of body water by the antipyrine dilution method (Steele *et al.*, 1950; Keys and Brožek, 1953) and of specific gravity by the method of underwater weighing have been made on the same men (Messinger and Steele, 1949; Osserman *et al.*, 1950). The two independent methods of assay gave closely agreeing results for total body water and total body fat. According to some investigators, the substitution of the antipyrine method for specific-gravity measurement is considered a valid means of eliminating subject cooperation required by underwater weighing.

In a study of the human body during infancy, childhood, and adolescence, Boyd (1933) related specific gravity to stature and to age. For children at midrespiration she derived the following equations:

Specific gravity = 0.95431 + 0.000402 × stature (cm.),
Specific gravity = 0.98705 + 0.002218 × age (years).

When these equations were applied to the children in our study, good agreement was found between the specific gravity on the basis of stature and on the basis of age. The average values for specific gravity derived from the study of Zook (1932) on 164 boys, aged 5–19 years, agree with those obtained by Boyd. In obtaining the values with which to calculate the specific gravity of our children, Boyd's results were averaged with the smoothed values for the boys in Zook's study. The calculated specific gravity of our children averaged 0.999 for the age group 4–6 years, 1.006 for 7–9 years, and 1.011 for 10–12 years. The formula developed (Morales *et al.*, 1945) for estimating fat in adults from specific gravity was not applicable to children.

Estimations of body fat *in vivo* were also made from total body water by means of equations developed for children (Friis-Hansen *et al.*, 1951) as well as equations developed for adults and adapted to children. From the studies on children the fat content of our subjects averaged 22, 24, and 28 per cent of the body weight for the three age groups (Table 21). Methods developed on adults, including the use of formulas based on standard weight (McCance and Widdowson, 1951) and creatinine-excretion data (Miller and Blyth, 1952), gave slightly lower fat values. In general, the results agree with the estimated specific gravity and subcutaneous fat findings in indicating that our children possessed a moderate amount of body fat. Evidence was obtained in our metabolic-balance studies that

TABLE 21

ESTIMATED FAT CONTENT OF BODY WEIGHT

	AVERAGE AGE GROUP					
	4–6 Years		7–9 Years		10–12 Years	
PROCEDURE USED	Fat (Kg.)	Per Cent of Body Weight	Fat (Kg.)	Per Cent of Body Weight	Fat (Kg.)	Per Cent of Body Weight
Derived from studies on children*	4.0	22	6.0	24	9.5	28
Adapted from studies on adults:						
Using standard weight:†						
Based on chronologic age...	3.0	16	3.6	15	5.4	16
Based on anatomic age.....	2.8	15	3.6	15	5.4	16
Using urinary creatinine:‡....						
Based on chronologic age...	3.1	17	4.8	19	8.1	24
Based on anatomic age.....	1.9	10	5.3	21	9.2	27

* Friis-Hansen *et al.* (1951).
† McCance and Widdowson (1951).
‡ Miller and Blyth (1952).

the growth taking place in the children was adding tissue of a structural and functional character. This type of growth was evidenced by the retention of excess cations, that is, the excess of the electropositive minerals (calcium, magnesium, sodium, and potassium) over the electronegative minerals (phosphorus, sulfur, and chlorine). On the basis of both chronologic and anatomic age the children were within the normal range with respect to standard weight. Measurement by the skin-fold method on the biceps, in accordance with the Franzen technique (1929), also indicated moderate fatness. These observations, therefore, indicate that they were well nourished but were not obese.

LEAN-BODY-MASS EVALUATION

Evaluations of body water and body fat provide a means of estimating lean body mass (Table 22). In estimating lean body mass from total body water (Friis-Hansen *et al.*, 1951), the average values for the three age groups were found to be 78, 76, and 72 per cent of the body weight. The values derived from fat content

TABLE 22

ESTIMATED LEAN BODY MASS IN BODY WEIGHT

PROCEDURE USED	AVERAGE AGE GROUP					
	4–6 Years		7–9 Years		10–12 Years	
	Lean Body Mass (Kg.)	Per Cent of Body Weight	Lean Body Mass (Kg.)	Per Cent of Body Weight	Lean Body Mass (Kg.)	Per Cent of Body Weight
Derived from studies of body water of children*............	14.5	78	18.8	76	24.6	72
Adapted from studies of adult fat content:†						
Based on chronologic age.....	15.5	84	21.2	85	28.7	84
Based on an atomic age......	15.7	85	21.2	85	28.7	84
Adapted from adult oxygen consumption:						
Based on chronologic age‡....	16.5	89	18.1	73	30.0	88
Based on anatomic age‡......	17.1	92	17.4	70	29.1	85
Based on height and weight§..	15.7	85	14.2	57	27.8	82
Adapted from adult urinary creatinine-excretion studies:‡						
Based on chronologic age.....	15.4	83	20.0	81	26.0	76
Based on anatomic age.......	16.6	90	19.5	79	24.9	73

* Friis-Hansen *et al.* (1951).
† McCance and Widdowson (1951).
‡ Miller and Blyth (1952).
§ Behnke (1953*a*, 1953*b*).

(McCance and Widdowson, 1951) were somewhat higher but showed no change with age. No age trend would be expected, since our adjustment of these data assumed the same body composition for children and adults. In selection of the factor for converting body water to lean body mass, however, we chose a higher factor for childhood. It seemed appropriate to use the 73.2 factor for children in the conversion of the values from body water (Friis-Hansen *et al.*) rather than the lower factor of 70 for adults. Had the adult factor been applied, the results would have agreed with those obtained from fat by McCance and Widdowson.

Lean body mass may also be estimated by independent methods, such as measurements of oxygen consumption, urinary excretion of creatinine per 24 hours, urinary nitrogen excretion, and storage of nitrogen by the metabolic-balance method. Basal metabolic rate and creatinine excretion have long been associated with the amount of protoplasmic tissue present in the body. A close relationship would be expected, therefore, between the amount of lean body mass and the amount of basal heat produced and the creatinine excreted in a 24-hour period, referred to a square meter of body surface area.

Assuming that lean body mass has on the average the same relative composition during childhood and adulthood, we adapted the equation developed by Miller and Blyth (1952) to children, using the determined values of basal oxygen consumption:

Lean body mass =

$$\text{Standard weight} \left(-0.08943 + \frac{0.92674 \text{ Oxygen consumed}}{\text{Oxygen standard}} \right).$$

The standard values for oxygen consumption were those of Lewis *et al.* (1943) and Kenyon *et al.* (1954). The percentage of lean body mass obtained by this procedure was comparable to the values obtained by methods involving the measurement of either body water or body fat. Behnke's data (1953*a*, 1953*b*) for adults were adapted to boys by the following equations:

Lean body mass =

$$\frac{\text{Standard weight}}{46.54575} \left(\frac{74.1 \text{ Cal. hr. }^{-1}}{\text{Cal. hr. }^{-1} \text{ standard}} - \frac{35.26 \text{ Height}}{\text{Standard height}} \right).$$

The results of these various determinations are given in Table 22.

A study of urinary nitrogen excretion offers other means of evaluating body composition of children. Numerous investigators have found linear relationships between basal metabolic rate and daily urinary creatinine-excretion rate when results are derived from body weight in kilograms, stature in centimeters, and surface area in square meters. In evaluating the amount of lean body mass by means of creatinine excretion, the equation of Miller and Blyth (1952) for adults was converted to apply to children:

$$\text{Lean body mass} = \text{Standard weight} \left(0.2548 + \frac{0.51296 \ \text{Creatinine}}{\text{Standard creatinine}} \right).$$

The standard creatinine values used were those of Clark *et al.* (1951). By this method of analysis of body-weight composition in childhood, lean body mass averaged 83, 81, and 76 per cent on the basis of chronologic age, and 90, 79, and 73 on the basis of anatomic age, for the three age groups.

It can be said that lean body mass, as calculated from the total body-water values given by Edelman *et al.* (1952), compares favorably with the results on our children obtained by applying Behnke's equation based on oxygen consumption, height, and weight and adjusted for 10 per cent essential fat.

SIGNIFICANCE OF THE RESULTS

The methods adapted and applied *in vivo* to the estimation of composition of body weight of children, with special reference to

TABLE 23

BODY COMPOSITION

COMPONENT	AVERAGE AGE GROUP		
	4–6 Years	7–9 Years	10–12 Years
Body size:			
Gross weight, kg.	18.5	24.8	34.1
Stature, cm.	109	127	141
Surface area, sq. m.	0.746	0.942	1.167
Specific gravity	0.999	1.006	1.011
Body fat, per cent of body weight*.	22	24	28
Body water, per cent of body weight:			
Total†.	57	56	53
Extracellular‡.	21	21	19
Intracellular.	36	35	34
Protoplasmic mass, per cent of body weight:			
Lean body mass§.	78	76	72
Cell mass‖.	57	55	53
Cell solids#.	21	20	19

* Body weight minus lean body mass.

† Estimates based on weight and surface area (Friis-Hansen *et al.*, 1951).

‡ Derived from total water by conversion factor of 21.7/59 (McCance and Widdowson, 1951).

§ Derived from total water on basis of 73.2 per cent water in lean body mass.

‖ Lean body mass minus extracellular water.

Lean body mass minus total water, or lean body mass $\times$ 0.268.

total body water, extracellular and intracellular water, fat, and metabolically active protoplasmic mass—considered also as lean body mass or cell mass—have yielded significant information in terms of *in vivo* composition of body weight in childhood (Table 23 and Fig. 4). The methods adapted in calculating or estimating body composition of healthy, normal children are sufficiently sensitive to show slight changes during childhood, as demonstrated in Table 23. Furthermore, these results correspond favorably with the few direct chemical analyses that have been made on children's bodies after death. They also verify the observation that the chemical growth patterns during these years of childhood are remarkably similar.

With the assumptions made, with the hazards incurred when procedures developed for adults are adapted and applied to children, and with the relatively few subjects observed at certain age levels, it seems more than chance that such remarkably close agreement was reached in the prediction of composition of body weight of living children through the use of independent, direct and indirect, and physical and chemical measurements. The fact that successive observations were made and longitudinal data accumulated on the same children while they were maintained on a known adequate diet and lived under favorable environmental conditions contributes to the accuracy of the determinations and measurements from which the predictions of body composition were made.

CHAPTER SIX

Chemical Anthropology

What is needed today is less of theory and more of facts upon which to build a more substantial conception of growth, and to formulate its fixed characteristics in words.

WHITE HOUSE CONFERENCE ON CHILD HEALTH
AND PROTECTION (1932a)

Just as physical anthropology is concerned with the measurements of the human body and its parts, so chemical anthropology is concerned with the measurement of the nutrients consumed and the chemical units laid down in the body as a whole or in its various tissues. Chemical procedures may be directed toward evaluation of the body composition, of changing structures of the body, of physiologic adaptation during growth, and of the interdependencies of nutrients in the body during the attainment of growth and maturation.

The comprehensive observations made in our study of nutrition, physical and chemical growth, and development have provided an opportunity to expand and extend the scope of physical anthropology to include chemical anthropology and, at the same time, to explore the relationships that may exist between them. The information obtained contributes to our knowledge of the chemical processes of growth, the formation of chemical units of growth, and the way in which one measurement may be conditioned by another in the body's effort to maintain a homeostatic internal environment and body composition while contributing new chemical units for enlarging the size and function of the body with age.

CHEMICAL BASIS OF LIVING GROWTH

Living growth is a process characterized by the utilization of nutrient substances differing more or less from those composing the living body. The organism must be capable of taking the relatively complex components of foodstuffs, converting them into smaller and simpler molecules, selecting those required, and then synthesizing or refashioning the simpler molecules into complex chemical units that are characteristic of the organism itself. By processes of digestion the food is first broken down and changed to a suitable form for active participation in body chemistry and is then assimilated. Assimilation encompasses absorption, retention, and utilization. Each of the nutrients assimilated makes a specific contribution to the formation, maintenance, and function of parts of the body or the whole of the human organism. In the mature body which is maintaining weight, the anabolic and catabolic processes are in balance. During growth, however, the anabolic or rebuilding processes predominate.

When studying the characteristic chemical anatomy of the body, the chemical anthropologist measures the amount of nutrients and other chemical units taken into the body and their physiologic progress through the digestive, absorptive, and excretory processes and determines the amounts used for maintenance and nourishment of the body tissues and in the fabrication of the new units of growth. The various methods used for determining physical and chemical growth rates become more meaningful when they are presented against a background of the physiologic processes that are brought into play and are essential for the attainment of maintenance and growth with the enlarging or changing functions of the body.

To show some of the interrelationships between physical measurements and chemical growth determinations of the human body, those metabolic phases will be included which are primarily concerned with the chemical anatomy of the soft tissues—muscle, neural, and organ, in particular—and of the hard skeletal tissues. Our discussion will present certain phases of nitrogen, calcium, and mineral metabolism in relation to age, change of body size, maturation, and body composition during the physiologic adjustments and adaptations of childhood.

The construction of protoplasmic tissue—true living growth—involves particularly the assimilation of nitrogen, sulfur, phosphorus, calcium, magnesium, potassium, sodium, and chlorine. For instance, nitrogen, sulfur, and part of the phosphorus are used largely as structural components in the protein-lipid combination of the body cells, whereas potassium, sodium, chlorine, and some of the phosphorus serve a functional purpose in maintaining the electroneutrality of the tissues and an equitable osmotic environment for proper distribution of intracellular and extracellular fluids. Calcium, magnesium, and the remaining phosphorus, in association with other elements, function largely in skeletal growth and maintenance.

Some of the procedures which may be used by the chemical anthropologist and which were included in our study are as follows:

I. Metabolic-balance procedure
 A. Determination of difference between analyzed nutrients in the food consumed and their outgo in urine and feces: protein (nitrogen), heat of combustion of carbohydrates, fat, and total energy; total electropositive minerals (calcium, magnesium, potassium, and sodium); total electronegative minerals (phosphorus, chlorine, and sulfur).
 B. Relationship of nutrients in the metabolic balance, for example, calcium to phosphorus, nitrogen to phosphorus, nitrogen to potassium, nitrogen to sulfur, phosphorus to potassium; excess anions or cations stored; protein as related to total energy, or energy from carbohydrate and fat. To permit a more precise study of their combining power and physiologic significance, we have recorded the major electropositive and electronegative minerals in milliequivalents in addition to their weight.
II. Nitrogen distribution in the urine
 A. Determination of nitrogen partition: total nitrogen, urea nitrogen, creatinine nitrogen, creatine nitrogen, uric acid nitrogen, ammonia nitrogen, and estimated basal nitrogen.
 B. Relationships of total nitrogen excretion to creatinine, to creatinine coefficient, to sulfur, and to carbon.
III. Basal oxygen consumption and basal heat production
IV. Estimation *in vivo* of body composition
 A. Estimation of the composition of the living body: total fat, total body water and its component parts (intracellular and extracellular), protoplasmic mass.
 B. Evaluation from basal heat production, specific gravity, creatinine excretion, nitrogen and mineral metabolic balances; nitrogen and mineral content of blood serum and erythrocytes.
V. Physical measurements
 A. Anthropometric measurements including weight, length, width, circumference, and subcutaneous tissue.
 B. Estimation of physical build.

STANDARDS OF REFERENCE

A variety of measurements reflects the lability of the body structure and the active response of the growing individual to the many exogenous and endogenous factors that are brought to bear on it in the process of living. The quantitative determinations made on children do not have the precision of the fundamental sciences, since they are subject not only to errors of experimental technique but also to variations due to external and internal environments, as reflected in different physiologic states and processes, and to the varying degrees of rapidity with which some children pass through various phases of the growth cycle. Although the results of observations show great complexity and may defy at present an explanation of which is cause and which is effect, the recording of new and various types of measurement should permit the development of better techniques in the future and more precise information on the fundamental character of growth and physiologic function.

The inherent physical, chemical, and functional adaptation and maturation of the body is accomplished through an increase in body weight, height, surface area, and changes in visceral organs and body composition. Functional changes accompanying dimensional and ponderal growth are attained through enlargement or change in the energy-releasing organs—nervous, endocrine, and digestive systems—and in the cardiac, respiratory, and renal systems. Although these various components are all integral parts of the growth and differentiation processes, each advances in its own way and at a different rate, owing to certain geometric interrelations, mechanical tensions, and degrees of chemical maturity to which the body is subject. Although technical difficulties encountered in measurement of surface area and of *in vivo* body composition provide results which must be considered as approximate, these results, nevertheless, are useful in establishing trends and relationships.

The various measurements of growth differ: stature is a one-dimensional measurement; surface area is two-dimensional; and weight is essentially three-dimensional (Scammon, 1930; Ashworth and Brody, 1933). It is generally alleged that surface area, which changes in proportion to the *square* of linear size, shows characteristics similar to those that distinguish the various progressions in stature, namely, a rapid growth in infancy and early childhood, followed by a period of slow increment in middle childhood, a second period of rapid growth prior to puberty, and a terminal phase of slower increment in adolescence. Body weight, or volume, changes in proportion to the *cube* of linear size. Gross body weight is subject to large variations in amounts and proportions of protoplasmic mass, water, and fat; the lean body mass is the only component that attains approximate chemical maturity and therefore a constant composition sometime in late childhood. Relative increments are quite unlike in magnitude, as shown by the fact that stature increases nearly three and one-half fold, surface area seven fold, and body weight twenty fold between birth and early maturity (Scammon, 1930). Because of these widely different rates of growth, the referral of any measurement of food intake (Fig. 6), or assimilation, to the various standards of reference of body weight, height, surface area, and age may not yield corresponding trends. This means not that the results are inconsistent but rather that their interpretation is dependent on the growth pattern of the standard applied. Growth in size is also influenced by adjustments in body form and by change in the center of gravity of the body in order to meet mechanical stress and strain.

ASSIMILATION OF NUTRIENTS

There exist in the body many integrated factors which control or direct the chemical reactions involved in assimilation of foodstuffs. These well-organized processes by which food is converted into energy and living tissue are in part understood, though much still remains unknown. Even a relatively slight change in the nature of one of the many chemical reactions proceeding in the living body may result in an alteration of digestion, absorption, retention, or utilization of the food factors and thereby change the course and intensity of inherent growth by failing to nourish the body adequately.

The utilization of energy, protein, and other nutrients is directly dependent on intake, at least to the extent that an individual cannot accumulate the optimal quantities of nutrients or expend the proper amount of energy unless the materials are made available for use. The metabolic-balance procedure is the most direct meas-

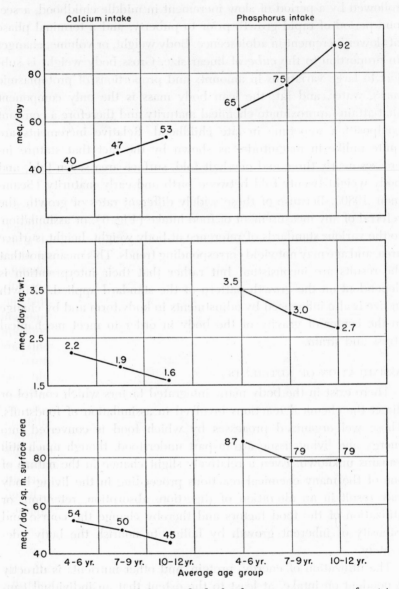

Fig. 6.—The influence of the standard of reference on measures of nutrient intake.

urement of requirements for growth and development and is concerned primarily with dietary utilization. During growth and development there is an accumulation of nutrients in new tissues, the total amount depending on the intensity of growth, as is demonstrated by positive metabolic balances; that is, the food intake is greater than the outgo in urine and feces. In growth, therefore, anabolism must exceed catabolism to allow for increasing structure and function accompanying physical growth.

When the metabolic-balance technique and other diverse but related chemical and physical procedures are applied over a period of months in the study of the chemical growth of children, it is possible to observe simultaneously many physiologic activities of the body and to ascertain trends of physiologic performance accompanying growth and development. When experimental errors of techniques and controls have been reduced to the minimum, and the nutritional stability of the subject has been established, it becomes possible to differentiate and to measure in chemical units the protoplasm and skeletal tissue laid down in the body over a period of time. The simultaneous observation of basal metabolic rate and excretion of various chemical components in the urine, together with nutrient assimilation, provides results which may be studied in relation to biologic adaptation and attainment of living growth in physiologic time. The organism absorbs much more of the nutrients from the intestinal tract than it selects and retains from the metabolic pool (Fig. 7).

Whereas carbohydrates and lipids from various sources of plant and animal foods differ only in a minor degree in their nutritive value, proteins are unique in that certain of them are incapable of supporting growth when they are the only protein constituent of a diet otherwise adequate. The reason for nutritional deficiency of certain proteins is the complete absence, or partial lack, of certain amino acids in their chemical makeup; these are known as essential amino acids, since they cannot be synthesized in the body and must be furnished as such in the diet. The primary function of dietary proteins is to supply a suitable mixture of amino acids of proper amounts and proportions for the synthesis of body-tissue proteins. The digestive juices contain specific enzymes for hydrolyzing the dietary proteins to amino acids, and the body cells and fluid tissues possess enzymes, hormones, vitamins, and other nutrients for synthesizing the amino acids to body proteins. The amino acids may be utilized by the body either for maintenance and function of existing tissues and construction of new body proteins and of other amino acid components or as a source of energy. When the amino acids are used in energy metabolism, they are converted into nitrogen-free intermediates and ultimately into urea, which is excreted in that form in the urine.

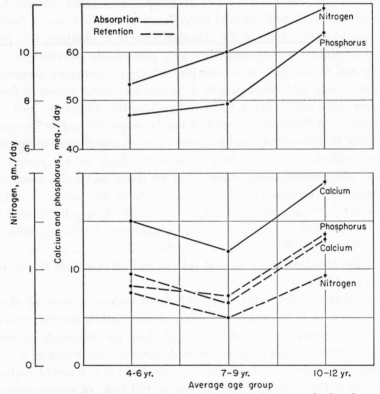

Fig. 7.—Retention and absorption of nitrogen, calcium, and phosphorus at each of three age levels.

Energy intake is paramount to the development and activity of the living body; consequently, emphasis is given to utilization of food for energy. The food must furnish a caloric intake above the critical minimum value in order to prevent the utilization of dietary amino acids and tissue proteins for energy. There is an optimal energy intake for nitrogen retention which varies with the physiologic state, age, sex, and activity of the individual. Addition of extra energy in the form of carbohydrate or fat, to an adequate diet generally leads to nitrogen retention and is usually stored as fat; therefore, it exerts a marked sparing action in human subjects for some time after its administration.

The results of determinations of energy and of nitrogen utilization reflect the influence of factors that modify the changes in structure and function which are taking place concurrently in the child's body. Retention of nitrogen for tissue construction is depressed when the energy intake is insufficient. Sometimes the rate of increase in body weight exceeds the accretion of nitrogen by far. At other times there is no gain in body weight for a time, although nitrogen is being retained. Changes in gross body weight may not be a true measure of chemical growth, even when the dietary is excellent with respect to all other known essential nutrients.

There is evidence of a dynamic relationship between the nitrogen balance and energy intake. The nitrogen balance is affected by a reduction in energy intake below normal, by increased energy expenditure, and by addition of energy-yielding nutrients to adequate diets. On a fixed and adequate protein intake, energy intake may become the determining factor in the nitrogen balance and therefore in protoplasmic growth.

In our children there was a delicate balance between the dynamics of energy and protein metabolism during protoplasmic growth (Macy and Hunscher, 1951; Macy, 1952). Biochemical individuality may be modified by both rate and quality of growth. For this reason the food supply must furnish sufficient energy to provide for a reasonable reserve, which may be drawn upon in times of unusual stress or augmented needs. The boys of this study had an average energy food intake of 2,099 Cal. per day. Only a net value of 1,933 Cal. daily was available to the body, owing to the energy loss in the urine and fecal excretion. The average daily basal energy requirement of the body and the specific dynamic action of the food in metabolism accounted for an additional 1,264 Cal., leaving 669 Cal. on the average for activity. This amount of available energy would seem adequate to take care of the activity of these normal children (Table 24).

The average protein absorption was approximately 64 gm. daily. If the dietary protein was assumed to have a biologic value of 50 per cent, double the basal protein loss, there would still be available for metabolic activity a surplus of 42–54 gm., or 168–216 Cal., daily (Table 25).

TABLE 24

AVERAGE DAILY ENERGY EXCHANGE

MEASUREMENT	AVERAGE AGE GROUP		
	4–6 Years	7–9 Years	10–12 Years
Potential food energy, Cal.*	1,803	2,051	2,443
Potential heat lost, total Cal.†	137	162	199
In urine, Cal.	62	76	92
In feces, Cal.	75	86	107
Physiologic fuel value, Cal.‡	1,666	1,889	2,244
Basal heat production, Cal.	983	1,061	1,399
Per cent of net Calories.	59	56	62
Specific dynamic action of foods, Cal.§	100	113	135
Energy available for activity, Cal.‖	583	715	710
Per cent of physiologic fuel value	35	38	32

* Gross Calories determined by heat of combustion of food.
† Heat of combustion of urine and feces.
‡ Heat of combustion of food minus heat loss through urine and feces.
§ Six per cent of the net or physiologically available energy.
‖ Fuel value minus basal heat production and specific dynamic action of food.

CHEMICAL UNITS OF GROWTH

Protein and minerals are a part of every cell in protoplasmic and skeletal tissues and are essential during growth. The chemical processes which characterize living matter take place in salt solutions, which permit the minerals to be transported and easily distributed throughout the body. They maintain osmotic, ionic, and acid-base equilibriums of the body and aid in regulating the chemical processes. The body cannot function without protein and minerals which have been absorbed and retained. In their utilization the body rearranges and adjusts the protein and minerals which it already possesses. Under conditions of normal growth every kilogram of body substance must receive its full complement of the different nutrients before the body can furnish material for synthesis of new tissues. The change in the composition of the body resulting from growth can be assessed from two viewpoints, namely, relative and absolute growth. Relative growth involves the comparative amounts of the various components which measure the alterations of chemical structure, whereas absolute growth involves the actual amount of minerals stored in the body and is the measurement of the requirements of growth.

In consideration of the physiologic significance of protein and the major mineral components of a body fluid, however, it is necessary

TABLE 25

AVERAGE DAILY PROTEIN EXCHANGE

MEASUREMENT	AVERAGE AGE GROUP		
	4–6 Years	7–9 Years	10–12 Years
Protein intake, total gm...................	61	71	82
Nitrogen intake, mg./basal Cal...........	9.96	10.67	9.40
Nitrogen excretion, total gm..............	9.03	10.82	12.22
Urine, gm............................	7.93	9.62	10.88
Feces, gm............................	1.10	1.20	1.34
Fecal nitrogen, mg./gm. dry food intake..	3.1	3.0	2.8
Nitrogen absorption, total gm.............	8.69	10.12	11.81
Per sq. m. surface area, gm..............	11.6	10.8	10.0
Nitrogen retention, total gm..............	0.76	0.50	0.93
Nitrogen retained, mg./basal Cal.........	0.77	0.47	0.66
Available protein energy, Cal.*...........	245	283	329
Protein metabolized as energy, Cal.†......	210	255	288
Basal protein loss, gm.‡..................	6.09	7.29	9.88
Basal protein requirement, gm.§..........	12.18	14.58	19.76
Surplus protein available, gm.‖...........	42.13	48.67	54.05

* Protein in grams × 4.

† Urinary nitrogen × 26.51 (1 gm. of urinary nitrogen represents 26.51 Cal. derived from protein).

‡ Difference between total urinary nitrogen and urea nitrogen × 6.25.

§ Assuming a biological value of 50 per cent for dietary protein utilization.

‖ Protein absorbed minus estimated basal protein loss.

to study the chemical entities in terms of their activities or functional units. The weight of a substance, taken alone, gives limited information on its role in the living organism. For this reason it is more meaningful to weigh reactions of the body in terms of chemical equivalents, that is, comparable activity or combining power for equal volumes. The contemplation of physiologic units or of chemical substances in terms of their equivalence permits a more adequate description of their presence in living systems than does comparison of weight. Since the physiologist is concerned with relatively small amounts of chemical substances, and because physiologic units have greater significance in the study of the chemistry of growth, we have recorded the values of protein and the major minerals in milliequivalents.

The changing requirements of our children on a standardized diet are illustrated by their fluctuating nitrogen absorption and retention (Table 26). The quantity of nitrogen absorbed is a measure of nitrogen metabolism in the body and is much greater than the nitrogen retained, which is subject to unknown skin losses and therefore cannot be measured accurately. Nitrogen absorption increases with age, body size, and protein and energy intake, but the increase is not so rapid as the increase in weight, surface area, and

TABLE 26

NITROGEN ABSORPTION AND RETENTION

UNITS OF MEASUREMENT	NITROGEN ABSORPTION			NITROGEN RETENTION		
	4–6 Years	7–9 Years	10–12 Years	4–6 Years	7–9 Years	10–12 Years
Meq./day............	2.11	2.46	2.87	0.185	0.122	0.226
Meq./day/sq. m. S.A...	2.82	2.62	2.43	.243	.129	.194
Meq./day/kg. wt.......	0.11	0.10	0.08	.010	.005	.007
Meq./day/kg. L.B.M...	0.14	0.13	0.12	0.013	0.006	0.009

lean body mass. The nitrogen retention, however, fluctuates, being least for the middle age group.

An individual child may not necessarily follow the average trend for nitrogen or the other elements. Also, the time chosen for the study of an individual may influence his individual trend. On the other hand, the trend of the group may be minimized by the statistical process of averaging.

During growth there is an accumulation of both electropositive and electronegative minerals in new tissues, the amount depending on the rate of the growth (Tables 27 and 28). The relationship between the gross amount of positive minerals—calcium, magnesium, sodium, and potassium—and negative minerals—phosphorus, sulfur, and chlorine—retained is determined by the relative demands for material with which to construct hard and soft tissues. The absorption and retention of total anions and total cations follow the general course of nitrogen.

The anion phosphorus is one of the most widely distributed elements in food intake and most generally used in all phases of body structure, metabolism, and function. In many systems of metabolism it is a dominant factor in the maintenance of neutrality and other phases of internal environment; in the enzyme systems that control utilization of energy, protein, and other nutrients; and in the construction and physiologic function of protoplasm and body tissue,

TABLE 27

ABSORPTION AND RETENTION OF ANIONS WITH GROWTH

UNITS OF MEASUREMENT	ABSORPTION			RETENTION		
	4-6 Years	7-9 Years	10-12 Years	4-6 Years	7-9 Years	10-12 Years
Total anions:						
Meq./day	177	196	242	22.0	16.4	32.1
Meq./day/sq. m. S.A.	237	208	206	29.2	17.5	27.6
Meq./day/kg. wt.	9.6	7.9	7.1	1.16	0.67	0.94
Meq./day/kg. L.B.M.	12.2	10.4	9.8	1.52	0.87	1.30
Phosphorus:						
Meq./day	47	49	64	8.3	7.2	13.5
Meq./day/sq. m. S.A.	62	51	55	11.0	7.9	11.7
Meq./day/kg. wt.	2.5	2.0	1.9	0.44	0.30	0.40
Meq./day/kg. L.B.M.	3.2	2.6	2.6	0.57	0.38	0.55
Sulfur:						
Meq./day	37	43	55	4.2	2.6	8.2
Meq./day/sq. m. S.A.	50	46	47	5.5	2.6	7.0
Meq./day/kg. wt.	2.0	1.7	1.6	0.21	0.10	0.24
Meq./day/kg. L.B.M.	2.6	2.3	2.2	0.29	0.14	0.33
Chlorine:						
Meq./day	93	104	123	9.5	6.6	10.4
Meq./day/sq. m. S.A.	125	111	104	12.7	7.0	8.9
Meq./day/kg. wt.	5.1	4.2	3.6	0.51	0.27	0.30
Meq./day/kg. L.B.M.	6.4	5.5	5.0	0.66	0.35	0.42

both hard and soft. Therefore, any disturbance in total phosphorus metabolism may be reflected in a number of metabolic systems and thus alter the course of growth and development at any time. In the children of our study the trends of absorption and retention of the total phosphorus, with the exception of surface area as the standard of reference, followed the general pattern of nitrogen and total anions.

Sulfur is essential primarily for protein formation, because the sulfur-containing amino acids, cystine and methionine, are characteristic of the body. Therefore, sulfur and nitrogen retentions may be expected to run about parallel, provided that the diet contains adequate amounts of all the essential amino acids. In our study small variations in absorption levels of sulfur on the basis of the different standards of reference may account for the trend differing from that of nitrogen absorption. The metabolic technique is, perhaps, not accurate enough to show precise trends in absorption

TABLE 28

ABSORPTION AND RETENTION OF CATIONS WITH GROWTH

UNITS OF MEASUREMENT	ABSORPTION			RETENTION		
	4-6 Years	7-9 Years	10-12 Years	4-6 Years	7-9 Years	10-12 Years
Total cations:						
Meq./day.............	174	191	238	30.4	25.5	42.0
Meq./day/sq. m. S.A....	234	202	203	40.4	27.0	36.0
Meq./day/kg. wt........	9.4	7.7	7.0	1.58	1.03	1.23
Meq./day/kg. L.B.M....	12.0	10.2	9.7	2.10	1.36	1.71
Calcium:						
Meq./day.............	15	12	19	9.7	6.6	13.2
Meq./day/sq. m. S.A....	21	12	16	12.8	7.2	11.4
Meq./day/kg. wt........	0.8	0.5	0.6	0.51	0.28	0.38
Meq./day/kg. L.B.M....	1.0	0.6	0.8	0.67	0.35	0.54
Magnesium:						
Meq./day.............	10	10	12	3.7	3.3	3.6
Meq./day/sq. m. S.A....	13	11	10	4.9	3.5	3.1
Meq./day/kg. wt........	0.5	0.4	0.3	0.20	0.13	0.11
Meq./day/kg. L.B.M....	0.7	0.5	0.5	0.26	0.18	0.15
Potassium:						
Meq./day.............	58	64	78	6.0	6.5	7.4
Meq./day/sq. m. S.A....	78	68	67	8.1	6.8	6.3
Meq./day/kg. wt........	3.2	2.6	2.3	0.29	0.26	0.22
Meq./day/kg. L.B.M....	4.0	3.4	3.2	0.41	0.34	0.30
Sodium:						
Meq./day.............	91	105	129	11.0	9.1	17.8
Meq./day/sq. m. S.A....	122	111	110	14.6	9.5	15.2
Meq./day/kg. wt........	4.9	4.2	3.8	0.58	0.36	0.52
Meq./day/kg. L.B.M....	6.3	5.6	5.2	0.76	0.48	0.72

and retention when the differences between age-group averages are small. The loss of sulfur and nitrogen through the skin may also be a factor in the pattern of retention values.

Chlorine is distributed throughout the body and is contained in all body secretions and excretions. It is stored in limited quantities in skin, subcutaneous tissue, and skeleton. We found that the absorption and retention of chlorine followed the general course of nitrogen and total anions.

The amount of calcium retained in any length of time depends on factors involving the physiologic state of the individual organism and on chemical factors associated with food. An individual experiencing rapid skeletal growth, or one with a subnormal calcium concentration in body tissues, may require large amounts of this element to maintain a satisfactory physiologic state, although some studies indicate that adjustment to reduced calcium intake may occur (Nicholls and Nimalasuriya, 1939). Calcium makes up a large proportion of the mineral cations stored and is the major constituent of bone. Bone construction, therefore, is indicated by a storage either of calcium alone or of total mineral cations. Approximately twice as much calcium was absorbed as was retained at each of the three average age levels during childhood (see Fig. 7). The calcium absorption followed an independent course with age, whereas the trend of calcium retention was the same as the retention of nitrogen and the total minerals.

Magnesium is associated with calcium in skeletal formation and is present in the soft tissues and body fluids, yet knowledge of its specific physiologic function in human nutrition is meager. Magnesium has been shown to function as an essential component of the enzyme system involved in the breakdown of carbohydrate in muscle metabolism. With minor differences the trends of magnesium and calcium absorption and retention were similar.

Potassium is an essential part of the physicochemical structure of the cell. Although it has the ability to move into the cells as the protoplasm increases (Fenn, 1940) and pass into the blood during increased muscular activity or rate of metabolism, it is the chief intracellular cation and is associated with most of the fundamental properties of protoplasm and cells. Therefore, it is intimately related to vital processes. Potassium is associated with nitrogen in the formation of soft tissue in the body, this by virtue of its activity in relation to cellular water. When nitrogen is stored in the form of new protoplasmic protein, potassium is retained in sufficient quantities to meet the intracellular fluid needs. Potassium is known to be held within the cell, although the factors controlling its entrance into and its egress from the cell are unknown (Shohl, 1939). This element participates in the control of body neutrality. The trend with age of absorption of potassium for our children was similar to that of nitrogen. The loss of potassium through the skin may influence the retention trend, which differs from that of nitrogen. If 30 per cent of the retained amount was lost through the skin, then approximately 182 mg. of potassium was actually retained, on the average, per day.

Sodium is found in plasma and extracellular fluids of the body, although some is associated with cartilage and muscle cells. Sodium functions with chloride and bicarbonates in the control of the concentrations of the body fluids. It is the predominant positive mineral element in the extracellular fluid. The actual amounts of sodium and potassium retained per day are comparatively small, but the ratio between these two elements in the diet is considered of greatest practical importance. The trend with age of absorption of sodium was similar to that of nitrogen and potassium. The course of retention levels, with the exception of sodium on the basis of surface area, agreed with nitrogen. If we assume that 12 per cent of retained sodium was lost through the skin, then approximately 256 mg. was retained per day by the boys in our study.

Although it is known that retention values include the cumulative errors of the metabolic-balance procedures and analytic techniques, especially insofar as skin losses are concerned, these values seem to have significance in spite of technical errors. Nitrogen, sulfur, and a portion of the phosphorus are used primarily as structural components in the protein-lipid components of the cell; potassium, sodium, chlorine, and some of the phosphorus serve a functional purpose in maintenance of the electroneutrality of the tissues with an equitable distribution of intracellular and extracellular fluids; nitrogen, phosphorus, and possibly sulfur are distributed in the lipid components. The degree of storage of any one or all of these elements will be influenced by the food intake and the current nutritive needs of the individual.

The ranges found in the retention ratios of nitrogen to sulfur, nitrogen to phosphorus, nitrogen to potassium, and calcium to phosphorus indicate the variability of the nutritive needs of the body and the body's ability to choose those elements in quantities which best meet its current structural and functional requirements. Because of the importance of nitrogen and phosphorus in numerous organic compounds associated with soft-tissue and fluid-tissue for-

mation and maintenance in growth, nitrogen-to-phosphorus retention ratios are of especial significance (Table 29). The calcium-to-
phosphorus ratios are associated with hard-tissue versus soft-tissue
formation.

Special consideration has long been given to calcium and phosphorus on account of the close relationship of these minerals to the
formation of the skeleton. In the construction and maintenance of
the bony tissue of the body, portions of the calcium and the phosphorus retained become a part of the skeletal structure, and the
remainder participates as structural components of protoplasmic

TABLE 29

RETENTION AND ABSORPTION RATIOS

Ratio	Average Age Group		
	4–6 Years	7–9 Years	10–12 Years
Retention:			
Nitrogen* to phosphorus:			
Milligram basis	5.3	4.0	4.0
Milliequivalent basis	0.022	0.017	0.017
Nitrogen to potassium:			
Milligram basis	3.2	2.0	3.2
Milliequivalent basis	0.031	0.019	0.030
Nitrogen to sulfur:			
Milligram basis	11.2	12.2	7.1
Milliequivalent basis	0.044	0.047	0.028
Potassium to sodium:			
Milligram basis	0.9	1.2	0.7
Milliequivalent basis	0.5	0.7	0.4
Calcium to phosphorus:			
Milligram basis	1.34	1.06	1.14
Milliequivalent basis	1.17	0.92	0.98
Absorption:			
Nitrogen to phosphorus:			
Milligram basis	10.8	12.0	10.7
Milliequivalent basis	0.045	0.050	0.045
Nitrogen to potassium:			
Milligram basis	3.8	4.0	3.8
Milliequivalent basis	0.036	0.038	0.037
Nitrogen to sulfur:			
Milligram basis	14.5	14.7	13.4
Milliequivalent basis	0.057	0.057	0.052
Potassium to sodium:			
Milligram basis	1.09	1.05	1.03
Milliequivalent basis	0.6	0.6	0.6
Calcium to phosphorus:			
Milligram basis	0.39	0.28	0.34
Milliequivalent basis	0.32	0.24	0.30

* Based on the Van Slyke factor for protein: milliequivalents per liter = 2.43 gm./
100 ml.

and fluid tissues or as functional components in intermediary metabolism. The small portion of calcium present in the body elsewhere than in bone exists largely as calcium salts in the body fluids, such as the plasma, or in combination with some organic radicals. The phosphorus of the body is distributed among a greater number of tissues than the calcium, its primary functions being the construction of high-energy organic phosphate esters used in phosphorylating intermediates in enzymatic metabolic processes and in the construction of nucleic acids for structures in both the nucleus and the cytoplasm of the cells. It is beyond the purpose of this volume to consider the many factors that affect the metabolism of the minerals in skeletal growth, such as level and relative proportions of minerals, fat content and vitamin content of dietary intake, the hormones, and the acid-base equilibrium of the body. There are many physiologic and chemical factors, however, which may influence calcium utilization, including the endocrine system, which superimposes an additional influence on the amount of calcium that is used at any one time.

The chemical composition of the body accretions at the three average age levels in our study varied. The fabricated body substances in the 4–6-year age group was relatively richer in the cellular phase—retained nitrogen $\times$ 6.25—and the skeletal phase—retained calcium and total cations—than in the 7–9-year group (Tables 27 and 28). There was a different type of physicochemical adjustment and chemical growth taking place at 7–9 years, with a lowered rate of construction of tissues and an obvious reorganization in the biologic systems of growth leading to soft- and hard-tissue construction, as shown by the trend in the storage of nitrogen, calcium, phosphorus, the total cations and the total anions, and the retention ratios of calcium to phosphorus and of potassium to sodium. In the 7–9-year age period there was a tendency for soft-tissue formation to take greater precedence over construction of skeletal tissue, as indicated by the reduced retention ratios of nitrogen to phosphorus, nitrogen to potassium, and calcium to phosphorus and the increased retention ratio of potassium to sodium. The 10–12-year group built soft and hard tissue at a greater rate than the 7–9-year group, but relatively more hard tissue than soft tissue. When the general pattern of chemical growth of the 4–6-year age group was compared with that of the 10–12-year-olds on the basis of total daily retentions of nitrogen, calcium, phosphorus, total cations, and total anions, there was an increase shown in the amount of hard and soft tissue being formed at the older age level. The calcium-to-phosphorus ratios indicated that relatively more soft tissue than hard tissue was being formed at the 10–12-year age level than at the 4–6-year level, whereas the potassium-to-sodium retention ratio seemed to indicate the reverse. The possible losses through the skin, however, must be taken into consideration in these interpretations.

There is a tendency for the younger child to build a body composition richer in protoplasm when the muscles and parenchymatous organs are growing rapidly and acquiring their functional power. The 7–9-year age group showed an adjustment in the pattern of body components laid down, with a slowing-down in the protoplasmic increase and the continuation of a slow bone increase. This observation on hard-tissue formation corroborates the work of Maresh (1955) on the linear growth of the long bones of extremities and confirms the description of the 7–9-year period as one of "latency." It might be termed a period of preparation for the remarkable changes in the chemical pattern of body composition, for approaching changes in body function, and for a more dominant control due to hormonal and sex factors.

A study of excretions provides pertinent information on chemical growth. The nitrogen eliminated in the urine is derived from the products of digestion, absorption, and intermediary metabolism. Urinary nitrogen, which represented 83 per cent of food nitrogen and 89 per cent of the total excretion of nitrogen from the bodies of our children, had entered into the body economy, whereas the greater part of the 11 per cent found in the feces probably had not entered into the organism and had not been of biologic value. Some of the fecal nitrogen may arise from metabolic sources, but, in the main, the feces contain nitrogenous products of other origin—undigested food residues, gastrointestinal secretions or excretions, bacteria, and their by-products. No analytical method is available by which the fecal nitrogen which has been utilized by the body—metabolic origin—can be distinguished from the portion which has not been assimilated.

It has been found that a relationship exists between the metabolic fecal nitrogen and the intake of dry matter (Mitchell and Bert, 1954). This relationship is found to be close when the intake of food is sufficient for maintenance of body weight and when the fiber content of the diet is low. Although increasing the fiber content of the diet increases the proportion of metabolic fecal nitrogen to dry matter consumed, the inclusion of increased protein apparently does not disturb the ratio of metabolic fecal nitrogen to dry matter consumed. The metabolic fecal nitrogen represents wastages of body nitrogen that must be replaced to maintain the nitrogenous integrity of the body.

The daily dry weight of feces of our children (see Table 8) was variable but, on the average, increased from 16 gm. at 4–6 years, to 18 gm. at 7–9 years, to 22 gm. at 10–12 years. Both the fresh and the dry weights of feces were within narrow ranges of percentage of their respective fresh and dry weights of intake. For the age groups given, the fresh weight of the feces averaged 5.1, 5.1, and 4.7 per cent of the fresh food intake, respectively; the dry weight averaged 4.4, 4.5, and 4.5 per cent, respectively, of the dry food intake and 0.94, 0.97, and 0.93 per cent of the fresh intake. The average dry weights of the feces represented 18, 19, and 20 per cent of the fresh feces. The average daily fecal nitrogen based on dry matter consumed amounted to 3.1, 3.0, and 2.8 mg. per gram of dry food for the increasing age groups.

The excretion of urinary creatinine nitrogen is not affected to any great extent by depletion of protein stores until this depletion begins to reduce muscle mass, or by the feeding of different kinds of proteins, except when the organism is saturated with creatinine precursors. On the average diet the excretion of creatinine can be used as a reference with which the more variable components of the urine can be correlated. There is an increase in both the absolute and the relative excretion of creatinine, per kilogram of body weight, from birth to puberty.

Urinary nitrogen output on a protein-free diet is a measure of basal protein requirement and, together with basal heat production, is an important datum in the study of growth. Nevertheless, in our study of chemical growth in childhood, where it was so essential to maintain nutritional stability at all times, we did not believe that there was justification for subjecting the children to a deficient or low-protein diet even for a few days and thereby disturbing the nutritional status in order to obtain true endogenous nitrogen excretion. Therefore basal urinary nitrogen was not measured directly; an estimate was made, however, by indirect procedures.

Since the children were maintained on a diet composed of the same basic foods, qualitatively constant, adjusted to meet current growth and activity needs, it seemed reasonable to estimate the

TABLE 30

ESTIMATED BASAL URINARY NITROGEN

MEASUREMENT	AVERAGE AGE GROUP		
	4–6 Years	7–9 Years	10–12 Years
Urinary nitrogen partition, mg./day:			
Urea N	6,715	8,296	9,351
Ammonia N	228	268	369
Total creatinine N	296	360	392
Preformed creatinine N	156	218	292
Creatine N	140	142	100
Uric acid N	126	130	142
Total N*	7,690	9,463	10,932
Total basal urinary nitrogen, mg./day	975	1,167	1,581
Mg./day/sq. m	1,321	1,241	1,346
Mg./day/kg	52.7	47.1	46.4
Mg./day/kg. L.B.M.	67	62	64
Mg./day/basal Calorie	1.0	1.1	1.1

* Totals include some undetermined nitrogen.

total basal nitrogen portion of the urine via the results accumulated on the average daily urinary nitrogen partition (Table 30). It has been assumed that urea nitrogen is derived in large measure from food sources, whereas creatinine nitrogen, creatine nitrogen, and most of the uric acid nitrogen arise from continuing metabolic functions which are largely independent of food. Inasmuch as the children at each age level were on a protein intake 10 per cent or more above the National Research Council's recommended allowances, the urea nitrogen excretion would be expected to be high. In our children the analyzed urea nitrogen represented 87 per cent of the total urinary nitrogen excretion. Urinary nitrogen in the form of total creatinine nitrogen and uric acid nitrogen accounted for 5 per cent of the total nitrogen excretion. On the other hand, ammonia nitrogen excretion represented 3 per cent, and undetermined nitrogen 5 per cent, of the total urinary nitrogen excretion. Undetermined urinary nitrogen is comprised of certain minor constituents such as amino acid nitrogen and the nitrogen of urinary pigments. The accumulative errors involved in the determinations of total nitrogen and the nitrogen components affect the level of undetermined urinary nitrogen.

On the assumption that urea and probably some creatinine, creatine, and uric acid are of exogenous origin, the difference between the total urinary nitrogen and urea nitrogen would be a maximum estimate of basal urinary nitrogen, or approximately 13 per cent of the total urinary nitrogen excretion for our children. This maximum estimate, however, when considered in relation to basal Calories, gave 1.0 mg. of basal urinary nitrogen per Calorie at the 4–6-year age level and 1.1 mg. for the two older age groups, which are lower than the endogenous nitrogen factor of 2 mg. derived from a protein-low diet by Smuts (1935). Our figures were close to the value of 1.14 mg. obtained for adults by Bricker and Smith (1951), however. An important part of the total endogenous urinary nitrogen excretion is creatinine nitrogen. Investigators studying adults on a protein-low diet have reported creatinine nitrogen to represent approximately 25 per cent of the total endogenous nitrogen. When this value was applied to the data on children, however, the basal nitrogen obtained from creatinine excretion was higher than the maximum estimates derived from the difference between urea and total nitrogen excretion. In children some creatine is excreted in the urine and becomes a part of the endogenous urinary nitrogen discard. In our study the daily outgo of creatine nitrogen amounted to 140 mg., 142 mg., and 100 mg. for the three increasing age groups.

Most of the sulfur found in the urine results from protein metabolism. If the diet does not provide sufficient energy to meet growth and activity needs, an excessive amount of tissue protein will be metabolized to provide fuel, thus causing increased excretion of both urinary nitrogen and sulfur. The ratio of nitrogen to sulfur in the food and urine is significant, since they are both involved in protein metabolism (Table 31). Likewise, the nitrogenous and carbonaceous compounds—urea, uric acid, creatinine, creatine—of the urine are of interest, since they too give information on protein metabolism, inasmuch as they are oxidation products of protein metabolism. The ratio of carbon to nitrogen in the urine, together with the caloric value, gives information on the physiologic fuel value of protein. With an average daily urinary nitrogen excretion of 10 gm. in childhood, the carbon-to-nitrogen ratio was about

TABLE 31

AVERAGE DAILY CALCIUM, NITROGEN, SULFUR, AND
CARBON EXCHANGE IN METABOLISM

MEASUREMENT	AVERAGE AGE GROUP		
	4–6 Years	7–9 Years	10–12 Years
Food intake:			
Calcium, gm./day........	0.807	0.947	1.059
Nitrogen, gm./day.......	9.79	11.32	13.15
Sulfur, gm./day..........	0.681	0.786	1.009
Nitrogen-to-sulfur ratio...	14.4	14.4	13.0
Urinary excretion:			
Calcium, gm./day........	0.118	0.102	0.110
Nitrogen, gm./day.......	7.93	9.62	10.88
Sulfur, gm./day..........	0.532	0.648	0.749
Carbon, gm./day.........	....	8.6	8.6
Carbon-to-nitrogen ratio..	....	0.89	0.79
Nitrogen-to-sulfur ratio...	14.9	14.8	14.5

0.84. The average daily potential energy lost in the urine and feces amounted to 137 Cal., 162 Cal., and 199 Cal. for the three age groups, which was divided about equally between the urine and feces. The carbon-to-nitrogen ratio is an indicator of the completeness of utilization of carbon for energy and is of particular interest in abnormal metabolic states. Of the average daily intake of carbon (198 gm.), 8.6 gm. was excreted in the urine and 9.4 gm. in the feces. Approximately 92 per cent of the gross energy of the diet was available for body use.

Oxygen consumption is directly associated with the amount of active protoplasmic tissue present in the body and also may be greatly influenced by the rapidity with which protoplasm is forming. As would be expected, there was an increase in oxygen consumption with increasing physical size of our children (Table 32). It varies also with the amount, stage, and rapidity of development of the various body organs and tissues, since on a unit basis some tissues consume more oxygen than others.

Basal heat production and creatinine are associated with the amount and activity of the protoplasmic tissue present in the body

TABLE 32

STANDARDS OF REFERENCE OF METABOLIC ACTIVITY

MEASUREMENT	AVERAGE AGE GROUP		
	4–6 Years	7–9 Years	10–12 Years
Total:			
Oxygen consumption, ml. O_2/min.........	141	152	201
Total creatinine nitrogen, mg./day........	296	360	392
Preformed creatinine nitrogen, mg./day....	156	218	292
Per square meter surface area:			
Oxygen consumption, ml. O_2/day.........	190	161	173
Total creatinine nitrogen, mg./day........	404	395	335
Preformed creatinine nitrogen, mg./day....	209	231	250
Per kilogram of body weight:			
Oxygen consumption, ml. O_2/day.........	7.7	6.2	6.0
Total creatinine nitrogen, mg./day........	16.0	14.5	11.5
Preformed creatinine nitrogen, mg./day*...	8.0	8.7	8.5
Per kilogram of lean body mass:†			
Oxygen consumption, ml. O_2/day.........	9.7	8.1	8.2
Total creatinine nitrogen, mg./day........	20	19	16
Preformed creatinine nitrogen, mg./day....	10.8	11.6	11.9

* Generally referred to as creatinine coefficient.
† Fat-free body weight.

and with the rapidity of growth and maintenance of protoplasm. In our children basal heat production and total and preformed creatinine excretion increased with body size and age. Both result from the metabolic activity of all the individual body organs and tissues. Different organs, however, may have different rates of oxygen consumption; the rate of oxygen consumption is also influenced by the young and rapidly growing organism. The fact that oxygen consumption and creatinine are derived from different sources may account for the various patterns of growth when considered on the basis of different standards of reference. Metabolism was further evidenced by a considerable decrease in creatine nitrogen excretion during the 10–12-year age period, which was a significant indication of the approach toward maturity. The period between 7 and 12 years was one of continuous increase in both hard and soft tissue, but the rate of formation and the type of growth as well as the body composition were changing. The methods available for *in vivo* assessment of body composition permit an exploration of units of increase of the cellular metabolically active and the structural skeletal components.

In summary, the chemical anthropologist can measure, in chemical units, general body growth by unrelated, independent, direct and indirect methods. Living growth is the sum of the many structural, physiologic, and metabolic changes that occur in the various systems concerned with the increase in the body. It is generally accepted that fat and water additions to the body do not constitute true growth but that protein accretion to the cellular phase does. The lean body mass reaches chemical maturity during childhood with a more or less stabilized water content, and the skeletal portion remains at about 20 per cent of the body weight throughout life. The protoplasmic cellular component, which is a constant element of all normal body mass of a given species, is the center of metabolic activity. The skeletal component is a constant of the structural phase of the body. The accretions of the chemical units of nitrogen and calcium determined by the metabolic-balance procedure have been used as a measure of cellular and skeletal formation and to observe the metabolic patterns of protoplasmic and skeletal activity as the body adapts to growth and development or reacts to injury or processes of regeneration. The chemical anthropologist, therefore, can contribute to the scope of physical anthropology. Chemical procedures can be directed toward evaluation of chemical units of growth, of changing structures and composition of the body, of physiologic adaptation of growth and function to meet changing needs, and of interdependencies of chemical entities in terms of their equivalents, activities, and function during growth and maturation.

CHAPTER SEVEN

The Mosaic of Physical and Chemical Growth

In saying that life is the directing idea and evolutive force of the living being, I express merely the idea of a unity in the succession of all the morphological and chemical changes accomplished by the germ from the beginning to the end of life.

BERNARD (1865)

THE "MILIEU INTÉRIEUR"

Claude Bernard, the great pioneer physiologist and father of modern medicine, emphasized that a living being must be treated as a harmonious whole and that a special technique for experimentation be developed. His professional interest in physiologic questions concerning life-processes culminated in the publication of numerous expositions of the experimental method as applied to physiology and of the principle of scientific determinism on which it is based. The best known of these is *Introduction à l'étude de la médicine expérimentale,* published in 1865. It is said to be one of the few medical books which has not aged quickly (Sigerist, 1933) and is known to serve to this day as a constant inspirational tie between observational and experimental sciences. To Claude Bernard an experiment was simply an induced or provoked observation, and he believed that intuition or feeling gives rise to the experimental idea and that reason devises the actual experiment.

Although Bernard appreciated how difficult it is to devise a perfect experiment, it is his contribution to have described perfectly, and out of his own experience, the collaboration of mind and nature, of facts and ideas, which takes place in the experimental method. Moreover, he stressed that results of an experiment be noted with a mind stripped of hypotheses and preconceived ideas. He emphasized that the apparent spontaneity of living beings—the necessary

condition of natural phenomena—is determined in living bodies as
well as in inorganic bodies and that under identical conditions the
resulting phenomena will be similar, that is, the principle of determinism. In this connection he introduced the long-famous concept
of the *milieu intérieur,* showing that phenomena peculiar to living
beings such as mammals take place in a perfect internal environment.

Living or biologic growth is growth of a community of cells
with fixed boundaries, forming a mosaic of the different metaboliz-
ing systems. The cells within the body, particularly of higher organ-
isms, are bathed by fluids which constitute an inner environment,
the *milieu intérieur.* Life and growth of cells are possible only if the
composition of these fluids varies within extremely narrow limits.
The tendency of the living body is to maintain as constant as possible the composition of this internal environment, and, if the
dynamic equilibrium is slightly upset in one direction, reactions
take place which tend to restore the balance. Bernard's basic biologic
generalization therefore is a freedom within limits. He believed
that all vital mechanisms, varied as they are, have only one object—
that of preserving constant the conditions of life in the internal
environment, a concept which is the basis of general physiology and
biology.

The conception of the role of internal environment in the life of
the body as a whole has captured the imagination of physiologists
and biologists for a century. The revered modern physiologist
Walter B. Cannon (1932) called the process "homeostasis" in his
book *Wisdom of the Body.* Haldane (1931), in his *Philosophical Basis
of Biology,* emphasized the maintenance of body structure and the
fact that structure and activity cannot be separated, a phenomenon
which is the active manifestation of the persistent whole, that is, the
life of the organism. Whereas Claude Bernard regarded the blood
and lymph as internal environment, bathing all the living cells in the
body, Haldane points out that the environment of each cell depends
on the influence of the other cells, so that there is no common internal
environment but only a common element in the environment. Thus
blood bears to actual cell environment a relation similar to that of
the external environment, but of a much closer and more defined
sort. The living organism is ultimately dependent on external con-

ditions and on the integrative processes mediating the relationship between the organism and the external environment.

The concept of the internal environment has had marked influence on intricate physiologic and growth investigations. Henderson (1928) sought proof that internal environment is "fixed." At the same time Barcroft (1934) was impressed by the contrast between "fixed" and "free" internal environment. He observed that gross variations in internal environment do not result in devastating disturbances in such body functions as heart action, muscular efficiency, and kidney function; rather, variations in the internal environment may result in mental disturbance and lack of ability to concentrate, to think logically, and to pay attention. The implication therefore is that we can expect to find intellectual development only in an organism whose *milieu intérieur* has become fixed.

THE MOSAIC OF GROWTH

Of the many systems of the body concerned with growth, each can proceed at a different rate. Although the *modus operandi* of the processes of biologic growth and function may not be fully understood, it is evident that there are cellular changes, synergy of growth rates of all systems, and proportionate growth to permit developmental differentiation to proceed in a normal fashion. There are productive and non-productive substances associated with the increase in the size of the body. In general, an increase in body fat cannot be considered as growth, since it is not biologically active. On the other hand, as Behnke has emphasized throughout his work, a small amount of essential fat associated with vital function is necessary for life and metabolic functions. Different types of cells in the body have their own requirements for specific nutrients, or building blocks, in order to develop their unique cellular structure. Some biologic systems may be latent during certain phases of development; others may regress. Each system has a maximum rate at which it is able to maintain satisfactory co-ordination; if for some reason the special rate is submerged, growth differences take place (Willier *et al.*, 1955). Although the pattern of growth is little understood because of its great complexity, all the component systems are subject to a master control which leads to unification and equilibration of the many kinds and rates of growth in the body. The primary component of life and growth of the organism as a whole is protoplasm, which is pre-eminently composed of protein and is the leading controlling factor in the metabolic systems of the body.

Todd adopted the concept of the whole organism in his consideration of the biogenetic growth potential of the child (Krogman, 1951). Although he conceived of growing or increase in size, growing up or changes in body proportions, and maturing or the passage of biologic time in the tissues as complex and intricate processes, he noted the persistence of an orderly pattern of developmental growth under healthful conditions. Physical and physiologic adaptations take place in the structural parts of the body to permit the organism as a whole to function effectively while growing and in accordance with the stage of maturity. At the same time readjustments in the parts of the body and of the internal environment occur to meet the needs of new or, in some cases, enlarged structure and function. The skeleton and osseous centers of various joints have long served as the focal point of study of growth and development of body and mind (Rotch, 1908; Baldwin, 1921). The skeleton enlarges, matures, and grows together (Boyd, 1955).

Quantitative orderliness of physical constitution and physiologic process of mammals has been pointed out by Adolph (1949). As a basis of our study of the stresses incurred by the different rates of increase in size and metabolism of the body components, by changes in body proportions, and by maturation in accordance with biologic time, we observed a group of children during periods when certain readjustments in relation to the various structural parts involved were taking place. Periodic physical measurements, determinations of metabolic activity, and evaluation of body components simultaneously applied produced results which can be used to describe, in part, the trends and symmetry of developmental growth in healthy children. These findings lend themselves to scientific treatment by precise methods which the biologist may use in studying growth and functional differences among individuals. In this presentation only trends and interrelationships were sought. Hence the unweighted yearly age-group averages for children of 4–6 years, 7–9 years, and 10–12 years have been given, since these values correspond to the median chronologic age and are sufficiently refined for our present purpose. Individual growth will be considered subsequently.

Physiologic systems may differ at various degrees of maturity, as illustrated by the phenomena of the regression of the thymus, the decrease in the number of bones in the body, changes in the composition and structure of blood and other cell constituents, and changes in the relative composition of the major components of the body. It is possible that there are for growing children reversible physiologic systems that permit the body to adapt rapidly to the stress that may be caused by a sudden shift in rate in the formation of either hard or soft tissues or both, as in the case of a spurt in developmental growth. Sudden changes in the various types of biologic systems involved in growth and homeostatic control can bring into play a succession of adaptive physical, physiologic, and biochemical processes in order to maintain a harmoniously balanced functional state corresponding to the new status of maturity. Chemical adaptations likewise occur in order to provide and distribute those elements from the metabolic pool which are required to satisfy the current needs of the cells of bones, muscles, organs, and neural tissues undergoing an augmented rate of growth.

While the organism as a whole carries on the processes of growth and maintenance, physiologic regulatory mechanisms continually control, within limits, all activities. The internal environment acts so that body temperature is constantly maintained within a very narrow range. Oxidation processes provide all the energy expended by the body, whether the energy is employed to maintain body temperature, to support muscular activity, or to convert food substances into suitable form and incorporate them into body tissues as increments of living growth or in replacement and maintenance. Even the energy required to eliminate surplus, used, or unusable substances is regulated by the fluids of the body that bathe the individual cells.

HEMATOLOGICAL, CHEMICAL, AND STRUCTURAL STUDIES OF BLOOD

The degree to which the internal environment is disturbed and nutritional deficiencies exist in the bodily tissues has significance in studies of growth and development. Growth increases bodily nutritive requirements beyond the individual needs of maintenance, and, if these requirements are not currently met, nutritional inadequacy may result. The stress of greatly augmented growth may produce in tissues a deficiency of even greater consequence, resulting in conditioned or secondary nutritional inadequacy. Malnutrition or nutritional failure therefore may arise in spite of an adequate dietary. Unrecognized as well as obvious food allergies may exist in varying degrees and thereby interfere with food intake of sufficient quality and quantity or with proper gastrointestinal absorption and utilization of the nutrients that are consumed. When absorption from the intestinal tract is thus disturbed, anatomic, chemical, and physiologic changes may be impaired. Such conditioning factors are difficult to identify.

The function of the blood and other body fluids is for respiratory, nutritive, and excretory purposes and to maintain the water balance of the tissues. These fluids contain chemical substances and are the vehicles by which all tissues are protected and regulated.

The blood is a fluid tissue composed of innumerable chemical substances and various formed elements—red blood cells, or erythrocytes; white blood cells, or leucocytes; and platelets. Hematopoiesis is the production of all types of blood cells. Erythropoiesis, or formation of the red cells, takes place in the marrow of the bones. During their formation they pass through several stages of development involving varying physiologic activities and functions. The young cells possess a nucleus, whereas the older ones contain hemoglobins of different kinds, each possessing specific physicochemical characteristics, and some having immunological implications. The hemoglobin contains the protein globin and the pigment composed of porphyrin combined with iron. The hemoglobin serves as the vehicle for the vital transfer of oxygen from the lungs to the bodily tissues.

Red blood cells may vary in volume, weight, diameter, thickness, and content of hemoglobin. Sex, exercise, time of day, altitude, environmental temperature, change in water concentration of the blood, and emotional disturbances may affect the red blood cell count and hemoglobin content of the blood. Hematological observations, including cell volume, weight, diameter, thickness, water content, and specific gravity, provide information of significance on the size and shape of the red cells, their physicochemical behavior, and their physiologic activity or efficiency. Both the size and the activity of the erythrocytes are important to nutritive success in somatic structural growth and development. Table 33 presents the number of erythrocytes observed and their size and shape for the children of our study during three age periods. The degree of maturity of the red blood cells alters the chemical activity, since the reticulocytes have a high rate of respiratory metabolism, whereas

TABLE 33

HEMATOLOGICAL OBSERVATIONS DURING GROWTH

OBSERVATIONS	AVERAGE AGE GROUP		
	4–6 Years	7–9 Years	10–12 Years
Erythrocytes:			
Whole blood, millions/c. mm.	4.14	4.53	4.75
Hemoglobin, gm./100 cc.	12.6	12.3	12.9
Hematocrit, per cent	40	39	42
Corpuscular measurements:			
Volume, c.μ	83	88	89
Weight, $\mu\mu$g.	90	94	. . . .
Diameter, μ	7.3	7.3	7.4
Thickness, μ	2.0	2.1	2.1
White blood cells:			
Total per c. mm.	7,816	7,809	5,261
Polymorphonuclears, per cent	51	46	53
Lymphocytes, per cent	43	43	39
Monocytes, per cent	5.2	7.7	12.0
Eosinophiles, per cent	1.0	2.8	1.4

the mature erythrocytes have high oxidative and glycolytic metabolism.

According to our recorded observations (Macy, 1942), the concentration of minerals in the serum of children is strikingly constant, whereas the red blood cells exhibit more variability and appear to be more susceptible to environmental influences. The mineral distribution in the erythrocyte and plasma, or serum, indicates the ability of the organism to maintain normal function and equilibrium in the face of changes stimulated by growth and developmental processes and by environmental factors such as food and living conditions.

In the distribution of minerals between the plasma and red blood cells, most of the sodium of the blood resides in the serum, and the potassium in the cells; about twice as much chloride is allocated to the serum as to the cells (Table 34). Inasmuch as wide variations in size and weight of the erythrocytes may occur, values expressed in terms of concentrations per unit weight may mask important changes in the individual cell, which may have metabolic or structural significance. When considered in terms of composite weight

TABLE 34

BLOOD CHEMISTRY DURING GROWTH

DETERMINATIONS	AVERAGE AGE GROUP		
	4–6 Years	7–9 Years	10–12 Years
Plasma:			
Nitrogen, mg./100 ml.	1,002	1,165	....
Total lipid, mg./100 ml.	434	434	....
Serum:			
Calcium, mg./100 ml.	9.8	10.4	11.1
Phosphorus, mg./100 ml.	5.74	5.42	6.01
Sodium, mg./100 ml.	317	321	324
Potassium, mg./100 ml.	16.0	15.6	27.0
Chlorine, mg./100 ml.	359	367	365
Erythrocytes:			
Nitrogen, mg./100 gm.	4,433	4,810	....
Total lipid, mg./100 gm.	448	425	....
Sodium, mg./100 ml.	34	45	39
Potassium, mg./100 ml.	502	427	385
Chlorine, mg./100 ml.	181	180	193
Potassium-to-sodium ratio	14.8	9.5	9.9

per liter, the electrolytes—sodium, potassium, chloride—were more concentrated in the erythrocytes in children on the fixed dietary than in children on a self-selected diet (Macy, 1942). Furthermore, there was less variability in the individual determinations of the different mineral contents in the red blood cells, indicating greater standardization in the children being studied. Determination of the corpuscular weight composition verified the results obtained in terms of composite weight per liter. In spite of the changes taking place in the erythrocytes, the serum was able to maintain a constancy of internal environment by mobilization of base. In seeking indicators of stages in growth, development, and state of health in children of different races and ages, more attention should be given to the composition of erythrocytes and other individual cells.

The white blood cells, or leucocytes, possess a nucleus, and they are closely associated with the physiologic state of the body and with the immunity of the body. They possess mobility and the ability to engulf and ingest micro-organisms and foreign solid particles. The polymorphonuclear cells reflect the physiologic status of the myelogenous system of the body, the monocytes that of the reticuloendothelial system, and the lymphocytes that of the lymphatic system. The differential leucocyte count provides special information on the physiologic processes taking place in the body. The differential counts for our children are given in Table 33. The white cell count is also influenced by nutritive state, activity, and emotional disturbances as well as by infections and temperature.

The lipid and mineral content of tissues has been associated with physiologic activity and function. Increased physiologic activity in a tissue or organ is associated with increased amounts of phospholipid and free cholesterol. Lowered physiologic activity, degeneration, and retrogression may be accompanied by decreased quantities of these components and increased amounts of neutral fat and cholesterol esters (Williams *et al.*, 1941). High potassium-to-sodium ratios in tissues are related to a higher state of activity (Erickson *et al.*, 1937a, 1937b). The potassium-to-sodium ratio in erythrocytes of our children followed the same trend with age as calcium, nitrogen, total cation, and total anion retentions on the basis of weight and surface area.

Observations emphasize the fact that the erythrocyte is an organized entity that experiences reactions such as lower physiologic activity, retrogression, and degeneration similar to tissue cells. In view of the results obtained on the internal environment of the blood serum and the intact blood cell, it has been stated (Erickson *et al.*, 1937a):

A consideration of the growth processes (changing structure and function) in the light of both minerals and lipids of the plasma, together with the hematological observations, offers evidence suggesting that the concentration of minerals may indicate the ability of the organism to maintain equilibrium in spite of changing structure and function, whereas the lipids may indicate the progressive stages of development between infancy and maturity. Certain characteristic differences of the plasma lipid found between the neonatal period, preadolescence (5 to 9 years), and maturity suggest a fruitful field of investigation in extending the present data and exploring other periods of advancement, such as infancy, early childhood and puberty.

On the other hand, the greater constancy of lipids in the erythrocytes among individuals, as well as between children and adults, indicates that they are a more fundamental part of the structure itself and thus not as likely to be influenced by changes accompanying growth and environmental conditions. The minerals of the erythrocytes are probably more mobile constituents and may reflect the nutritional status and certain environmental influences, such as diet.

The maintenance of the proper acidity and alkalinity of the body tissues and fluids is essential for maintenance of life and health. The mechanisms largely responsible for maintaining constancy of chemical reactions in the blood and tissues are the elimination of carbon dioxide by the lungs, the excretion of acid by the kidney, and the buffer systems of the blood. The hemoglobin, sodium, potassium, calcium, magnesium, phosphorus, chlorine, and sulfur all participate in the ionic exchange that takes place in the blood plasma and cells for the maintenance of life-processes.

The progression of visible size and of invisible chemical additions of change in size, shape, and proportions forms the basic component of physical growth. There are, however, variations of the body systems which join together in action and form the basic theme of growth and development. They may be submerged from view at times and seem to disappear, but continuing observation demonstrates that, after the latency periods have passed, growth returns either in its original proportions or in some altered form.

TRENDS WITH AGE

This study of actual and relative measurements of body size, of body composition, and of body build and constitution demonstrates the value of parallel chemical and anthropologic measurements in depicting trends in physical, metabolic, and constitutional adjustments with age. These evaluations, combined with the assessments of stages of skeletal maturity by means of roentgenographic techniques, show whether the synergistic systems of growth are progressing in an orderly physiologic fashion in biologic time.

Physical Adaptation of the Body

Periodic anthropometric measurements, which have been designed for the study and description of certain features of the framework of the body and skeleton, provide an objective evaluation of the physical adjustments that accompany the enlargement of size, function, and components of the body. Table 35 presents the annual increase per se of the gross body weight, the change in dimensional measurements, and the enlargement in amounts of the major body

TABLE 35

AVERAGE ADAPTATION OF THE BODY WITH AGE*

ANNUAL INCREASE	AVERAGE AGE GROUP	
	59–95 Months	96–131 Months
Skeleton maturity†:.....	15.7 mo.	12.7 mo.
Body size:		
Gross weight.........	2.10 kg.	3.10 kg.
Stature..............	6.00 cm.	4.67 cm.
Surface area‡.........	0.065 sq. m.	0.075 sq. m.
Length:		
Stem..............	2.53 cm.	2.63 cm.
Leg...............	3.47 cm.	2.03 cm.
Head.............	0.50 cm.	0.00 cm.
Tibia.............	1.47 cm.	1.60 cm.
Width:		
Shoulder...........	0.80 cm.	0.83 cm.
Hip, intercristal....	0.67 cm.	0.47 cm.
Chest.............	0.60 cm.	0.77 cm.
Head.............	0.00 cm.	0.27 cm.
Depth, chest.........	0.33 cm.	0.40 cm.
Circumference:		
Head.............	0.67 cm.	0.30 cm.
Chest.............	1.33 cm.	2.33 cm.
Thigh.............	1.33 cm.	1.67 cm.
Abdomen.........	1.00 cm.	1.00 cm.
Upper arm........	0.40 cm.	0.50 cm.
Body composition:		
Cellular phase:		
Lean body mass....	1.43 kg.	1.93 kg.
Cell mass.........	1.03 kg.	1.43 kg.
Cell solids........	0.36 kg.	0.53 kg.
Water phase:		
Total body water...	1.07 kg.	1.40 kg.
Extracellular water..	0.40 kg.	0.50 kg.
Intracellular water..	0.67 kg.	0.90 kg.
Fat phase............	0.67 kg.	1.17 kg.

* Based on annual increase.
† Greulich-Pyle (1950), inspectional average.
‡ DuBois and DuBois (1916).

components based on advancement in age, size, shape, and maturity. It may be observed that the increases, absolute and relative, may differ at the developmental levels studied. The physical adaptations illustrated (Fig. 8) are based on the relative increase of body size between the ages of 59 and 95 months and between the ages of 95 and 131 months. The compilation of data permits a view of trends with respect to the relative alterations in physical and chemical measurements that may be associated with age and with change in total body size and composition (Fig. 9). Constitutional adjustments in the total skeleton, as well as in the proportions of the skeletal structure, and adaptations in ossification, with associated changes in metabolism and body composition, may be observed as they relate to the type of growth taking place.

Based on the annual increase in body size, the relative gain in gross body weight was less in the younger group of boys than in the older group, as illustrated in Fig. 8. The surface area, as obtained by the DuBois and DuBois (1916) formula, which takes into consideration both height and weight, increased at a more rapid rate in the younger boys than in the older group, owing to the fact that the relative height increase was greater in the young children.

The upper and lower parts of the body have different functions, and they adapt and mature at different rates. The dimensional measurements of total stature, length of head, stem, leg, and tibia, and width of shoulders and hips describe the rate of skeletal increase. The percentage increase, in relation to initial size, was more rapid in the younger boys than in the older ones. Conspicuous is the accelerated rate of growth of the legs in the younger children when compared with the older age group.

To accommodate the enlarging thoracic and visceral organs and their increasing capacity and function and the maturing skeletal portions of the shoulder and pelvic regions and the thoracic bony cage, the relative ponderance of the torso region changes. As would be expected, therefore, the relative increase in width, depth, and circumference of the chest was more rapid between the ages of 95 and 131 months than between the ages of 59 and 95 months. The rates of increase in the width of the shoulders and hips were the same in the younger group; however, as the children grew older, the shoul-

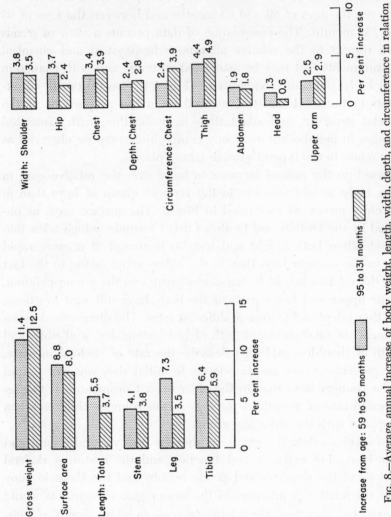

Fig. 8.—Average annual increase of body weight, length, width, depth, and circumference in relation to initial size at age intervals 59–95 months and 95–131 months.

der width change exceeded that of the hip width. With respect to the relative rate of increase in stem length, the younger children exceeded the older ones. The circumference of the thigh and upper arm, on the other hand, increased more rapidly in the older group of boys.

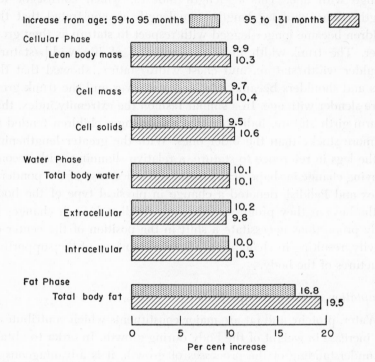

Fig. 9.—Average annual increase of body protoplasm, water, and fat in relation to initial composition at age intervals 59–95 months and 95–131 months.

Change in Body Type

When the form or function of the child's body is considered at different ages and developmental stages, certain relationships appear, although it may not be obvious which is cause or result. In translating physical dimensional measurements and evaluations of body composition into developmental growth patterns and biologic variability, ratios describe more accurately the physical and chemical adaptations that occur. Age progression in proportional parts of the body may be obtained, therefore, by observing the movement of a value in relation to some other value. Such observational ratings enhance the descriptions of differential growth and biologic variability with age.

The average rates of growth in the various segments of the body differ at different ages (see Chap. 3). Physical body types may change with age. The leg-length indexes, which consist of leg length/stature and leg length/stem length, demonstrated that the children became longer-legged with respect to stature as they grew older. The trunk-width indexes, composed of hip width/stature, shoulder width/stature, and chest width/stature, showed that the hips and shoulders became relatively narrower and the trunk grew more slender with age. In a similar fashion the extremity index, that is, arm girth/stature, indicated that the younger children tended to be more stocky than the older ones. With the greater lengthening of the legs in reference to stature, a relative slimming, with accompanying change in shape of the torso, and a decrease of the ponderal index and Pelidisi, denoted a change in physical type of the body of the boys as they progressed through childhood. Such changes in body proportions necessitate a shift in the position of the center of gravity, resulting in changing mechanical tensions of the supporting structures of the body.

Adaptation of Body Components

Water, protein, and fat are major constituents which contribute to the increase in weight of the body during growth. In order to obtain an understanding of the processes of growth, it is advantageous at each stage to have more specific information on the increment of each of these constituents which have been added. It is also essential to recognize gain in weight due to an increase in water or fat, which are largely metabolically inactive phases. The gain in weight of the cellular—protein—phase is the metabolically active portion of true living growth. By practical methods previously discussed, the body composition of our children has been estimated; this is illustrated in Figure 10.

Measurements of body composition by direct and indirect chemical procedures indicated changes with age. The younger children's body weights possessed a higher proportion of protoplasmic tissue than those of the older children, according to the Friis-Hansen water values converted to lean body mass (Figs. 10 and 11). The values for lean body mass decreased from 78 per cent at 4–6 years, to 76 per cent at 7–9 years, to 72 per cent at 10–12 years. The cell mass—lean body mass minus extracellular water, cell solids—lean body mass minus total water, and total water followed a similar

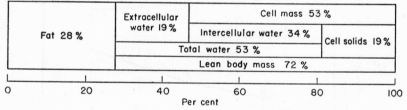

FIG. 10.—Body composition of boys (lean body mass, cell mass, cell solids, fat, extracellular water, and intracellular water) at each of three age levels.

course, with relatively higher concentrations in the younger bodies and lower concentrations in the older bodies. Conversely, the fat component of the body increased with age.

The relative change in body composition of the children in age groups 59–95 months and 95–131 months with respect to the cellular active phase, the total body water and its component parts—extracellular and intracellular body water—and the total body-fat phase is illustrated in Figure 9. Although the rates of increase in the cellular and water phases approximated each other for the two age groups, the cellular phase tended to increase more rapidly in the older group than in the younger group. The fat phase of the body composition increased more rapidly than either the cellular phase or the water phase, the rate of accumulation for ages 59–95 months and 95–131 months exceeding 16 and 19 per cent increase, respectively, in comparison with approximately a 10 per cent increase in the other phases.

Lean body mass, cell mass, cell solids, intracellular water, and fat

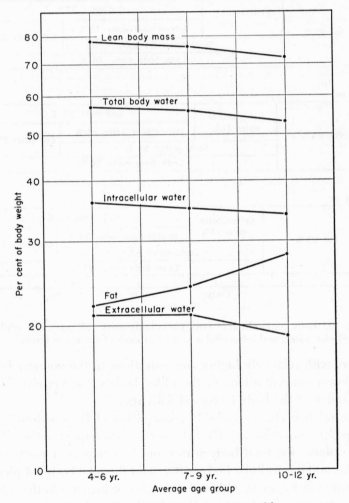

Fig. 11.—Change in body composition of boys

increased in quantity at a faster rate during the interval of 95–131 months than at the earlier age interval. The increase in the fat component, however, was much greater than that of the other constituents, accounting for the progressive increase in fat composition of the body with age. The estimated specific gravity as well as fat increased with age, results which would appear contradictory if the changes in the composition of the skeleton were not taken into consideration. According to Behnke and co-workers (1942), "of all the constituents of the tissues of the body, fat and bone appear to be the chief determinants of the ultimate values for specific gravity." We believe that the shift from cartilage to bone and the greater size and mineral content of the skeleton may account for the increase in specific gravity with age. More studies are needed to clarify the relationship of bone in different stages of development and degree of mineralization to specific gravity of the bodies of children.

Our children grew normally during the period of childhood, as judged by standard measurements (see Chap. 3). Their skeletal maturation was slightly under their chronologic age on the initial average-age basis, but it caught up with and exceeded chronologic age in the later age groups. This fact would indicate that bone formation is relatively on the increase in the older groups of children and might affect specific gravity of the body. Although this group of children was well nourished by the usual criteria at the three age levels, body measurements, specific-gravity estimation, and subcutaneous-tissue measurements showed that they possessed only a moderate amount of fat in their bodies and were not obese by the tests of standard weights and standard dimensions. As a matter of fact, the upper-arm girths at the two older age levels were within 5 per cent of the normal, according to the method of Franzen (1929). The subcutaneous-tissue measurement obtained over the biceps indicated more fat in the arm region of the children in the middle age group than of those in the upper age group, as shown in Table 36.

Extracellular water and lean body mass increased at a lower rate than the body fat, as shown by the extracellular water and lean-body-mass ratios with respect to body fat. In considering lean-body-mass changes on the basis of body surface, that is, in proportion to the square of the stature, no trend with age was observed. Lean body mass, however, is a measure of volume and is a cubic measure. Therefore, when lean body mass was considered in relation to the cube of the stature, there was a consistent decrease with age. This decrease of lean body mass with respect to the cube of height is independent of body fat.

At the same time, the relative body-fat composition increased with age and the relative amount of lean-body-mass component decreased, signifying that the bodies of the boys were undergoing changes in constitutional type. With increase in age, the children

TABLE 36

ADAPTATION OF BODY FAT WITH AGE

MEASUREMENT	AVERAGE AGE GROUP		
	4–6 Years	7–9 Years	10–12 Years
Upper-arm subcutaneous tissue/standard..	....	121	78
Upper-arm girth/standard...............	....	101	105
Specific gravity.......................	0.999	1.006	1.011
Extracellular body water/body fat.......	0.98	0.85	0.69
Lean body mass/body fat...............	3.62	3.13	2.59
(Lean body mass/height^2)$\times$100..........	0.122	0.116	0.124
(Lean body mass/height^3)$\times$10,000.......	0.112	0.092	0.088

showed an increase in the long bones of the legs and a definite change in the size and shape of the trunk, revealing a change in skeletal structure. Thus the children increased in size with age, but the rates of growth differed, as determined by anthropometric measurements. With respect to stature, the trunk of the body became narrower in width, especially at the hips, and shallower in the chest area. Such a change in body contour results in a preponderance of the trunk growth taking place in the thoracic region, thus accommodating the enlarging vital organs with their increasing function. This may be related to increase in fat content of the body.

Cellular and Functional Adaptation

The rate of growth of the cardiac, respiratory, and renal systems, of the digestive system, and of the muscular systems tends to follow the general pattern of increase of the body at different phases of the growth cycle, whereas other systems may proceed at their own particular time in the life-cycle and at different rates (Scammon, 1930). The amount and kind of metabolically active cellular substances present in the body at any one time thus influence the functional activities and may be reflected in the basal oxygen consumption and the basal urinary nitrogen excretion. What is even more significant is the fact that some body organs, tissues, and cells possess relatively greater power of oxygen consumption than others, although the basal oxygen determinations made on human subjects can give only the total combined consumption. Similarly, the urinary nitrogen excretion represents the results of total protein metabolism in the various kinds and amounts of metabolically active tissues in the body. The integration of chemical and metabolic determinations with physical dimensional measurements on the basis of a single unit or standard of reference may be complicated further by the fact that the rates of growth differ for the various reference standards of weight, height, and surface area. An interpretation of physical, chemical, and metabolic data on the basis of the different standard units, therefore, would not be expected to give consistent trends with growth. The metabolic rate, for example, tends to vary with surface area rather than weight. The larger individual differs in form from the small individual inasmuch as the pull of gravity on the body appears to vary with the cube of the linear size, whereas the tensile strength of the supporting structures such as limbs, muscles, and bones apparently varies with the square of linear size (Ashworth and Brody, 1933). In addition, the surfaces through which diffusion, metabolism, and excretion take place are believed to vary with the square of linear size.

Just as physical dimensional measurements demonstrate relative changes in body size, shape, and composition with age, so chemical determinations demonstrate accompanying cellular and functional adjustments. Positive relationships exist between basal energy, basal urinary nitrogen, and urinary creatinine-nitrogen excretion, primarily because they arise from the same physiologic mechanism associated with the metabolically active protoplasmic mass in the body. The trends obtained by the direct measurement of basal oxygen consumption of the cellular phase of the bodies of our children may be compared with the trends of basal urinary nitrogen excretion, an indirect measurement of the amount of protoplasm in the body at a given time (see Chap. 6).

In our study of children the average daily measurements of basal oxygen consumption and total urinary creatinine-nitrogen excretion indicated an increase with age and body size, whereas in relation to body weight a decrease was observed. When the results were considered on the basis of surface area, the youngest group possessed the highest oxygen-consumption values, the middle group possessed the lowest, and the oldest group values fell midway between the two younger groups. The finding that trends relative to units of body weight and surface may not be consistent with increasing age is not surprising, as each has its own characteristic cyclic rate. Though the progressions of body surface and weight are both characterized by rapid growth in early childhood, followed by a period of slow increases in middle childhood, and then a second period of rapid growth prior to puberty, they do not progress at the same rate (Scammon, 1930). Body composition, consisting largely of protoplasmic mass, fat, and water, may change with age and size. The amount, maturity, kind, and rate of increase of the protoplasmic mass determine the basal metabolic rate and therefore the basal urinary nitrogen excretion at any one time; the presence of fat and water in the body weight depresses metabolic activity. In an interpretation of data based on gross body weight or on a combination of factors including weight, as in the case of surface area, the relative proportion of lean body mass is of significance when values of basal energy and total creatinine nitrogen are under investigation.

Endogenous urinary nitrogen and its counterpart basal urinary nitrogen excretion, oxygen consumption, and urinary creatinine-nitrogen excretion are measures of cellular and functional activity taking place with increase in age, body size, and food consumption. Although endogenous urinary nitrogen excretion was not determined, the average daily total basal urinary nitrogen, roughly estimated on the basis of the difference between total urinary nitrogen and urea nitrogen, tended to increase with age. The actual amount of cell mass increased with age, whereas the relative amount of cell mass in body weight decreased during childhood. The oxygen consumption on the basis of cell mass was highest in the youngest age group—13.3 ml. per kilogram per minute in comparison with 11 ml. for the two older groups. Total urinary creatinine-nitrogen excretion interpreted on the basis of cell mass per day consistently decreased with age, namely, 27.9 mg., 26.3 mg., and 21.8 mg. for the respective age groups. Basal energy and creatinine-nitrogen excretion are not proportionately or functionally the same in metabolism. Creatinine excretion is related to body weight and musculature development, whereas basal energy seems to be closely associated with body surface. The elevated basal energy metabolism of the 4–6-year-old and 10–12-year-old children, on the basis of surface area per day, coincided with the rapid growth periods of body surface, in contrast to the slower-growing surface of the 7–9-year-olds. The estimated daily basal urinary nitrogen excretion paralleled the increased trend with age and size observed in the total creatinine-nitrogen excretion (see Chap. 6). On the other hand, when the basal daily nitrogen and total creatinine-nitrogen excretions were referred to body weight, the trends were not parallel. There are apparently many activities and internal compensations taking place during cellular and functional adaptations in the different epochs of life.

CHANGING TEMPO OF GROWTH

A harmonious blending of structure and function is essential to the fulfilment of the healthy human life-pattern; the link between chemical growth and physiologic rhythm of growth is movement in an orderly fashion in biologic time. Physiologic growth, being related to the developing pattern toward maturity of structure and function, must be permitted freedom if the inherent potentialities of the body system are to be realized. Many types of physicochemical data indicate that our children during their 4–12-year period in the life-cycle were increasing in size and scope of function and were undergoing internal chemical and metabolic reorganization, with resultant changes in type of growth. Conspicuous among the influences was a succession of changes in tempo of growth, a rapid increase during early childhood (4–6 years), a slowing-down during mid-childhood (7–9 years), and a more rapid increase in later childhood (10–12 years).

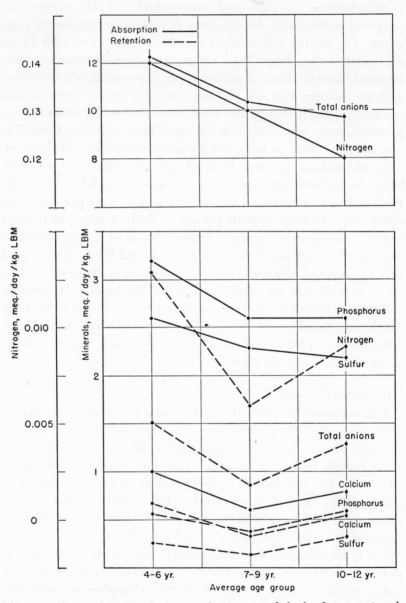

FIG. 12.—Retention versus absorption of nitrogen and the hard-tissue minerals at each of three age levels.

Although the children of this study consumed diets equal to or exceeding the recommended dietary allowances, and although their bodies were larger at each successive age period, the average daily requirements of protein and the major minerals fluctuated as judged by their absorption and retention (Fig. 12). These observations indicate changing metabolic activity for growth and development and corroborate the results obtained by direct and indirect measure-

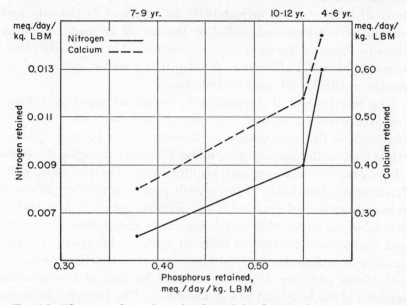
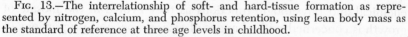

Fɪɢ. 13.—The interrelationship of soft- and hard-tissue formation as represented by nitrogen, calcium, and phosphorus retention, using lean body mass as the standard of reference at three age levels in childhood.

ments of protoplasmic cellular activity. There was a shift in type of growth taking place, with approximately equal proportions of skeletal and protoplasmic tissue construction at the youngest and oldest age levels, whereas a greater percentage of protoplasmic tissue was formed during mid-childhood. Singly and in combination, the many types of observations indicate a change in *tempo* and *dynamics* of the chemistry of growth in the developmental pattern of our children (Fig. 13).

In considering the retention ratios of nitrogen to potassium and nitrogen to sulfur for the three age groups, the results indicated that nitrogen was lowest in relation to potassium and highest in relation to sulfur at the 7–9-year level. The changing demands of the individual organs may condition the type of growth taking place at any stage of development.

By recording the various types of physicochemical measurements in childhood, we are made aware of the many existing mechanisms that participate, in one way or another, in providing the interplay of the chemical processes in the body—the response to different internal environments, to metabolic activity, and to the rate and amount of nutrients assimilated or thrown off as waste. Through these mechanisms the child may be transformed in an orderly physiologic fashion and allowed to develop into a mature person in accordance with his inherent biologic time.

This investigation of chemical and physical anthropology, extending over a quarter-century, has encompassed many more types of observations than are usually made on runabout healthy children while their bodies are adjusting to meet the ever changing demands of growth, development, and healthy living. For the most part, fundamental knowledge of the growth process is meager, although it has always been the subject of wonderment and study. It is understandable, therefore, that only a superficial description of changes and associations observed at different ages can be given. It is not possible to explain the essential life-processes or to segregate causes and effects with any degree of certainty because of the dynamic qualities of the body and lack of knowledge. The interplay between chemical and physiologic functions as they evolve in the mosaic of growth is concerned with changes of size, shape, and proportions of the body, with modifications in structure and function of organs and tissues, and with the tempo and dynamics of the maturation process. This area of study should challenge the novice as well as the veteran investigator. Each time a growing child is observed, he must be perceived in a new chemical, physical, and functional relationship. To conclude, we may repeat from our formulation of our basic concept of growth: "The greater the technical knowledge, the more comprehensive will be the understanding of the manifold elements of *normal* growth and maturation and those deviations which may lead to disease or failure in growth."

Bibliography

ADOLPH, E. F. 1949. "Quantitative Relations in the Physiological Constitutions of Mammals," *Science*, **109**, 579–85.

ALBRITTON, ERRETT C. (ed.). 1954. *Standard Values in Nutrition and Metabolism*. (Publication of National Research Council.) Philadelphia: W. B. Saunders Co.

ASHWORTH, URAL S., and BRODY, SAMUEL. 1933. *Decline of Endogenous Nitrogen Excretion per Unit Weight with Increasing Weight in Growing Rats, and Its Relation to the Decline in Basal Metabolism. Decline in Live Weight, Nitrogen and Energy Metabolism with the Advance of the Period of Nitrogen Starvation and the Influence of Live Weight and of Preceding Level of Protein Intake on These Declines and on the Survival Periods*. (Missouri Agr. Expt. Sta. Res. Bull. No. 190.) Columbia, Mo.

BALDWIN, BIRD T. 1921. *The Physical Growth of Children from Birth to Maturity*. ("University of Iowa Studies in Child Welfare," Vol. I, No. 1.) Iowa City, Iowa.

BALDWIN, BIRD T., BUSBY, LAURA M., and GARSIDE, HELEN V. 1928. *Anatomic Growth of Children: A Study of Some Bones of the Hand, Wrist, and Lower Forearm by Means of Roentgenograms*. ("University of Iowa Studies in Child Welfare," Vol. IV, No. 1.) Iowa City, Iowa.

BARCROFT, JOSEPH. 1934. *Features in the Architecture of Physiological Function*. New York: Macmillan Co.

BAYER, LEONA M. 1940a. "Build Variations in Adolescent Girls," *J. Pediat.*, **17**, 331–44.

———. 1940b. "Weight and Menses in Adolescent Girls, with Special Reference to Build," *ibid.*, pp. 345–54.

BAYLEY, NANCY, and PINNEAU, SAMUEL R. 1952. "Tables for Predicting Adult Height from Skeletal Age: Revised for Use with the Greulich-Pyle Hand Standards," *J. Pediat.*, **40**, 423–41.

BEHNKE, ALBERT R. 1941–42. "Physiologic Studies Pertaining to Deep Sea Diving and Aviation, Especially in Relation to the Fat Content and Composition of the Body," *Harvey Lectures*, **37**, 198–226.

———. 1953a. "Lean Body Weight in Relation to Basal (Standard) Metabolism," *Trans. New York Acad. Sci.*, **15**, 74–75.

———. 1953b. "The Relation of Lean Body Weight to Metabolism and Some Consequent Systematizations," *Ann. New York Acad. Sci.*, **56**, 1095–1142.

BEHNKE, A. R., FEEN, B. G., and WELHAM, W. C. 1942. "The Specific Gravity of Healthy Men, Body Weight Divided by Volume as an Index of Obesity," *J. Amer. Med. Assoc.*, **118**, 495–98.

BENEDICT, F. G. 1938. *Vital Energetics: A Study of Comparative Basal Metabolism*. (Carnegie Inst. of Washington Pub. No. 503.) Washington, D.C.

133

BENEDICT, F. G., and TALBOT, F. B. 1921. *Metabolism and Growth from Birth to Puberty.* (Carnegie Inst. of Washington Pub. No. 302.) Washington, D.C.

BERGER, EUGENE Y., DUNNING, MARCELLE F., STEELE, J. MURRAY, JACKENTHAL, ROSLYN, and BRODIE, BERNARD B. 1950. "Estimation of Intracellular Water in Man," *Amer. J. Physiol.,* **162,** 318–25.

BERNARD, CLAUDE. 1865. *Introduction à l'étude de la medicine expérimentale.* Paris: Baillière. Translation by H. C. GREEN. New York: Macmillan Co., 1927.

Biologists in Search of Material: An Interim Report on the Work of the Pioneer Health Center, Peckham. 1938. London: Faber & Faber, Ltd.

BOYD, EDITH. 1929. "The Experimental Error Inherent in Measuring the Growing Human Body," *Amer. J. Phys. Anthrop.,* **13,** 389–432.

———. 1933. "The Specific Gravity of the Human Body," *Human Biol.,* **5,** 646–72.

———. 1935. *The Growth of the Surface Area of the Human Body.* ("University of Minnesota, Institute of Child Welfare Monograph Series," No. 10.) Minneapolis: University of Minnesota Press.

———. 1955. "Pictorial and Graphic Analysis of the Body Build of One Boy," *Amer. J. Dis. Child.,* **89,** 332–40.

BOYD, EDITH, SCAMMON, RICHARD E., and LAWRENCE, DONOVAN. 1930. "The Determination of Surface Area of Living Children," *Proc. Soc. Expt. Biol. Med.,* **27,** 445–49.

BRICKER, MILDRED L., and SMITH, JANICE M. 1951. "A Study of the Endogenous Nitrogen Output of College Women, with Particular Reference to Use of the Creatinine Output in the Calculation of the Biological Values of the Protein of Egg and of Sunflower Seed Flour," *J. Nutrition,* **44,** 553–73.

BRICKER, MILDRED, MITCHELL, H. H., and KINSMAN, GLADYS M. 1945. "The Protein Requirements of Adult Human Subjects in Terms of the Protein Contained in Individual Foods and Food Combinations," *J. Nutrition,* **30,** 269–83.

BRODY, SAMUEL. 1945. *Bioenergetics and Growth, with Special Reference to the Efficiency Complex in Domestic Animals.* New York: Reinhold Publishing Corp.

BRODY, SAMUEL, PROCTER, ROBERT C., and ASHWORTH, URAL S. 1934. *Basal Metabolism, Endogenous Nitrogen, Creatinine and Neutral Sulfur Excretions as Functions of Body Weight.* (Missouri Agr. Expt. Sta. Res. Bull. No. 220.) Columbia, Mo.

BROŽEK, JOSEF, and KEYS, ANCEL. 1950. "Evaluation of Leanness-Fatness in Man: A Survey of Methods," *Nutrition Abst. and Rev.,* **20,** 247–56.

BROŽEK, JOSEF, HENSCHEL, AUSTIN, and KEYS, ANCEL, 1949. "Effect of Submersion in Water on the Volume of Residual Air in Man," *J. Appl. Physiol.,* **2,** 240–46.

CANNON, WALTER B. 1932. *The Wisdom of the Body.* New York: W. W. Norton & Co.

———. 1945. *The Way of an Investigator: A Scientist's Experience in Medical Research.* New York: W. W. Norton & Co.

CARREL, ALEXIS. 1935. *Man, the Unknown.* New York: Harper & Bros.

CHITTENDEN, RUSSELL H. 1907. *The Nutrition of Man.* New York: Frederick A. Stokes Co.

CLARK, LELAND C., JR., THOMPSON, HASKELL L., BECK, ELIZABETH I., and JACOBSON, WERNER. 1951. "Excretion of Creatine and Creatinine by Children," *Amer. J. Dis. Child.,* **81,** 774–83.

COOKE, ROBERT E., PRATT, EDWARD L., and DARROW, DANIEL C. 1950. "The Metabolic Response of Infants to Heat Stress," *Yale J. Biol. & Med.,* **22,** 227–49.

CORNER, GEORGE W. 1944. *Ourselves Unborn: An Embryologist's Essay on Man.* New Haven, Conn.: Yale University Press.

CURTISS, FRANK HOMER. 1898. "Some Investigations Regarding Loss in Weight and Gain in Height during Sleep," *Amer. Phys. Educ. Rev.,* **3,** 270–73.

DAVENPORT, C. B. 1926. "Human Metamorphosis," *Amer. J. Phys. Anthrop.,* **9,** 205–32.

———. 1937. "Some Principles of Anthropometry," *ibid.,* **23,** 91–99.

DRAPER, GEORGE. 1928. *I. Human Constitution: Its Significance in Medicine and How It May be Studied.* ("Beaumont Foundation Lectures Series," No. 7.) Baltimore: Williams & Wilkins Co.

DUBOIS, DELAFIELD, and DUBOIS, EUGENE F. 1916. "Clinical Calorimetry. X. A Formula To Estimate the Approximate Surface Area if Height and Weight Be Known," *Arch. Int. Med.,* **17,** 863–71.

DUBOIS, EUGENE F. 1936. *Basal Metabolism in Health and Disease.* 3d ed. Philadelphia: Lea & Febiger.

———. 1937. *The Mechanism of Heat Loss and Temperature Regulation.* ("Lane Medical Lectures.") Stanford University: Stanford University Press.

EDELMAN, ISIDORE S., HALEY, HAROLD B., SCHLOERB, PAUL R., SHELDON, DAVID B., FRIIS-HANSEN, BENT J., STOLL, GEORGES, and MOORE, FRANCIS D. 1952. "Further Observations on Total Body Water. I. Normal Values throughout the Life Span," *Surg. Gyn. Obs.,* **95,** 1–12.

EINSTEIN, ALBERT. 1950. *Out of My Later Years.* New York: Philosophical Library.

ELVEHJEM, C. A., and KREHL, WILLARD A. 1947. "Imbalance and Dietary Interrelationships in Nutrition," *J. Amer. Med. Assoc.,* **135,** 279–87.

———. 1955. "Dietary Interrelationships and Imbalance in Nutrition," *Borden's Rev. Nutrition Res.,* **16,** 69–84.

ERICKSON, BETTY NIMS, WILLIAMS, HAROLD H., HUMMEL, FRANCES COPE, and MACY, ICIE G. 1937a. "The Lipid and Mineral Distribution in the Serum and Erythrocytes of Normal Children," *J. Biol. Chem.,* **118,** 15–35.

ERICKSON, BETTY NIMS, WILLIAMS, HAROLD H., HUMMEL, FRANCES COPE, LEE, PEARL, and MACY, ICIE G. 1937b. "The Lipid and Mineral Distribution of the Serum and Erythrocytes in the Hemolytic and Hypochromic Anemias of Childhood," *J. Biol. Chem.,* **118,** 569–98.

FENN, W. O. 1940. "The Role of Potassium in Physiological Processes," *Physiol. Rev.,* **20,** 377–415.

FLORY, CHARLES D. 1936. *Osseous Development in the Hand as an Index of Skeletal Development.* ("Society for Research in Child Development Monographs," Vol. I, No. 3.) Chicago.

FOLIN, OTTO. 1905. "Laws Governing the Chemical Composition of Urine," *Amer. J. Physiol.,* **13,** 66–115.

FORBES, R. M., COOPER, A. R., and MITCHELL, H. H. 1953. "The Composition of the Adult Human Body as Determined by Chemical Analysis," *J. Biol. Chem.,* **203,** 359–66.

FRANZEN, RAYMOND. 1929. *Physical Measures of Growth and Nutrition.* ("School Health Research Monograph," No. 2.) New York: American Child Health Association.

FRIIS-HANSEN, BENT J., HOLIDAY, MALCOLM, STAPLETON, THOMAS, and WALLACE, WILLIAM M. 1951. "Total Body Water in Children," *Pediatrics,* **7,** 321–27.

GAMBLE, JAMES L. 1947. *Chemical Anatomy, Physiology and Pathology of Extracellular Fluid.* Cambridge, Mass.: Harvard University Press.

GOODMAN, NEVILLE M. 1952. *International Health Organizations and Their Work.* London: J. & A. Churchill, Ltd.

GREULICH, WILLIAM WALTER, and PYLE, S. IDELL. 1950. *Radiographic Atlas of Skeletal Development of the Hand and Wrist.* Stanford University: Stanford University Press.

HALDANE, J. S. 1931. *The Philosophical Basis of Biology.* London: Hodder & Stoughton, Ltd.

HASTINGS, A. BAIRD. 1940–41. "The Electrolytes of Tissues and Body Fluids." *Harvey Lectures,* **36,** 91–125.

HEELEY, ANN M., and TALBOT, NATHAN B. 1955. "Insensible Water Losses per Day by Hospitalized Infants and Children," *Amer. J. Dis. Child.,* **90,** 251–55.

HEGSTED, D. M., TSONGAS, A. G., ABBOTT, D. B., and STARE, F. J. 1946. "Protein Requirements of Adults," *J. Lab. Clin. Med.,* **31,** 261–84.

HENDERSON, LAWRENCE J. 1928. *Blood: A Study of General Physiology.* ("Silliman Lectures.") New Haven, Conn.: Yale University Press.

HIPPOCRATES. 1886. *The Genuine Works of Hippocrates.* Trans. FRANCIS ADAMS. New York: Wm. Wood Co.

HORVATH, S. M., and CORWIN, W. 1941. "Creatinine-Creatine Excretion in Schizophrenics," *Amer. J. Physiol.,* **133,** 679–85.

HUNTER, ANDREW. 1928. *Creatine and Creatinine, Monograph on Biochemistry.* New York: Longmans, Green & Co.

Inadequate Diets and Nutritional Deficiencies in the United States: Their Prevalence and Significance. 1943. (National Research Council Bull. No. 109.) Washington, D.C.: Food and Nutrition Board, National Research Council.

KELLY, HARRIET J. 1937. *Anatomic Age and Its Relation to Stature.* ("University of Iowa Studies in Child Welfare," Vol. XII, No. 5.) Iowa City, Iowa.

KELLY, HARRIET J., SOUDERS, HELEN J., JOHNSTON, A. THERESA, BOUND, LOUISE EMERSON, HUNSCHER, HELEN A., and MACY, ICIE G. 1943.

"Daily Decreases in the Body Total and Stem Lengths of Normal Children," *Human Biol.*, **15**, 65–72.

KENYON, FANNY, KELLY, HARRIET J., and MACY, ICIE G. 1954. "Basal Metabolism of Girls in the Great Lakes Region: Need for Continuous Promotion of Iodized Salt," *J. Amer. Dietet. Assoc.*, **30**, 987–90.

KEYS, ANCEL, and BROŽEK, JOSEF. 1953. "Body Fat in Adult Man," *Physiol. Rev.*, **33**, 245–325.

KEYS, ANCEL, BROŽEK, JOSEF, HENSCHEL, AUSTIN, MICKELSEN, OLAF, and TAYLOR, HENRY LONGSTREET. 1950. *The Biology of Human Starvation*, Vols. I and II. Minneapolis: University of Minnesota Press.

KLOPSTEG, PAUL E. 1955. "Role of Government in Basic Research," *Science*, **121**, 781–84.

KRAYBILL, H. F., HANKINS, O. G., and BITTER, H. L. 1951. "Body Composition of Cattle. 1. Estimation of Body Fat from Measurement *in Vivo* of Body Water by Use of Antipyrine," *J. Appl. Physiol.*, **3**, 681–89.

KRETCHMER, E. 1925. *Physique and Character: An Investigation of the Nature of Constitution and of the Theory of Temperament.* New York: Harcourt, Brace & Co.

KROEBER, A. L. (ed.). 1953. *Anthropology Today: An Encyclopedic Inventory.* Chicago: University of Chicago Press.

KROGMAN, W. M. 1951. "T. Wingate Todd: Catalyst in Growth Research," *Amer. J. Orthodontics*, **37**, 679–87.

LEE, DOUGLAS H. K. 1950. *The Physiology of Tissues and Organs: An Introduction to the Study of Systematic Physiology.* Springfield, Ill.: Charles C Thomas.

LEWIS, ROBERT C., DUVAL, ANNA MARIE, and ILIFF, ALBERTA. 1943. "Standards for the Basal Metabolism of Children from 2 to 15 Years of Age, Inclusive," *J. Pediat.*, **23**, 1–18.

LEWIS, ROBERT C., KINSMAN, GLADYS M., and ILIFF, ALBERTA. 1937. "The Basal Metabolism of Normal Boys and Girls from Two to Twelve Years Old, Inclusive," *Amer. J. Dis. Child.*, **53**, 348–428.

LILLIE, RALPH STAYNER. 1945. *General Biology and Philosophy of Organism.* Chicago: University of Chicago Press.

LUSK, GRAHAM. 1928. *The Elements of the Science of Nutrition.* 4th ed. Philadelphia: W. B. Saunders Co.

McCANCE, R. A., and WIDDOWSON, E. M. 1950–51. "Composition of the Body," *Brit. Med. Bull.*, **7**, 297–306.

———. 1951. "A Method of Breaking Down the Body Weights of Living Persons into Terms of Extracellular Fluid, Cell Mass and Fat, and Some Applications of It to Physiology and Medicine," *Proc. Roy. Soc.* (London), **B138**, 115–30.

MACK, PAULINE BEERY, BROWN, WALTER N., JR., and TRAPP, HUGHES DANIEL. 1949. "The Quantitative Evaluation of Bone Density," *Amer. J. Roent. Radium Therapy*, **61**, 808–25.

MACY, ICIE G. 1942. *Nutrition and Chemical Growth in Childhood*, Vol. I: *Evaluation.* Springfield, Ill.: Charles C Thomas.

———. 1946. *Nutrition and Chemical Growth in Childhood*, Vol. II: *Original Data.* Springfield, Ill.: Charles C Thomas.

MACY, ICIE G. 1951. *Nutrition and Chemical Growth in Childhood,* Vol. III: *Calculated Data.* Springfield, Ill.: Charles C Thomas.

———. 1952. "Importance of Calories in the Growth of Children," *Ann. New York Acad. Sci.,* **56,** 122–26.

MACY, ICIE G., and HUNSCHER, HELEN H. 1951. "Calories—a Limiting Factor in the Growth of Children," *J. Nutrition,* **45,** 189–99.

MACY, ICIE G., and KELLY, HARRIET J. 1956. "Body Composition in Childhood with Reference to *in Vivo* Chemical Analysis of Water, Fat, and Protoplasmic Mass," *Human Biol.,* **28,** 289–308.

MACY, ICIE G., REYNOLDS, LAWRENCE, SOUDERS, HELEN J., and OLSON, MARY B. 1940. "Normal Variation in the Gastrointestinal Response of Healthy Children," *Amer. J. Roent. Radium Therapy,* **43,** 394–403.

MANERY, J. F. 1954. "Water and Electrolyte Metabolism," *Physiol. Rev.,* **34,** 334–417.

MARESH, MARION M. 1955. "Linear Growth of Long Bones of Extremities from Infancy through Adolescence," *Amer. J. Dis. Child.,* **89,** 725–42.

MENDEL, LAFAYETTE B. 1904. "Some Aspects of the Newer Physiology of the Gastrointestinal Canal," *J. Amer. Med. Assoc.,* **43,** 1539–43.

———. 1923. *Nutrition: The Chemistry of Life.* New Haven, Conn.: Yale University Press.

MEREDITH, HOWARD V., and CULP, STANLEY S. 1951. "Body Form in Childhood: Ratios Quantitatively Describing Four Slender-to-Stocky Continua on Boys Four to Eight Years of Age," *Child Devel.,* **22,** 1–14.

MESSINGER, WILLIAM J., and STEELE, J. MURRAY. 1949. "Relationship of Body Specific Gravity to Body Fat and Water Content," *Proc. Soc. Expt. Biol. Med.,* **70,** 316–18.

METROPOLITAN LIFE INSURANCE COMPANY. 1953. *Health of Teen-Agers.* (Metropolitan Life Insurance Company Statistical Bulletin No. 34.) New York.

MILLER, A. T., JR., and BLYTH, CARL S. 1952. "Estimation of Lean Body Mass and Body Fat from Basal Oxygen Consumption and Creatinine Excretion," *J. Appl. Physiol.,* **5,** 73–78.

———. 1953. "Lean Body Mass as a Metabolic Reference Standard," *ibid.,* pp. 311–16.

MITCHELL, H. H. 1944. "Determination of the Nutritive Value of the Proteins of Food Products," *Ind. Eng. Chem.* (Anal. Ed.), **16,** 696–700.

MITCHELL, H. H., and BERT, M. H. 1954. "The Determination of Metabolic Fecal Nitrogen," *J. Nutrition,* **52,** 483–97.

MITCHELL, H. H., HAMILTON, T. S., STEGGERDA, F. R., and BEAN, H. W. 1945. "The Chemical Composition of the Adult Human Body and Its Bearing on the Biochemistry of Growth," *J. Biol. Chem.,* **158,** 625–37.

MORALES, MANUEL F., RATHBUN, EDITH N., SMITH, ROBERT E., and PACE, NELLO. 1945. "Studies on Body Composition. II. Theoretical Considerations Regarding the Major Body Tissue Components with Suggestions for Application to Man," *J. Biol. Chem.,* **158,** 677–84.

MORSE, MINERVA, CASSELS, DONALD E., and SCHLUTZ, FREDERIC W. 1947. "Available and Interstitial Fluid Volumes of Normal Children," *Amer. J. Physiol.,* **151,** 438–47.

MOULTON, C. R. 1923. "Age and Chemical Development in Mammals," *J. Biol. Chem.*, **57,** 79–97.

MUGRAGE, EDWARD R., and ANDRESEN, MARJORY I. 1936. "Values for Red Blood Cells of Average Infants and Children," *Amer. J. Dis. Child.*, **51,** 775–91.

NATIONAL NUTRITION CONFERENCE FOR DEFENSE. 1942. *Proceedings.* Washington, D.C.: Government Printing Office.

NEWBURGH, L. H. 1946. *The Significance of the Extracellular Fluid in Clinical Medicine.* ("Ernest A. Sommer Memorial Lectures.") Ann Arbor: J. W. Edwards, Inc.

NEWBURGH, L. H., and JOHNSTON, MARGARET WOODWELL. 1942. "The Insensible Loss of Water," *Physiol. Rev.*, **22,** 1–18.

NEWBURGH, L. H., JOHNSTON, M. W., LASHMET, F. H., and SHELDON, M. M. 1937. "Further Experiences with the Measurement of Heat Production from Insensible Loss of Weight," *J. Nutrition*, **13,** 203–21.

NICHOLLS, LUCIUS, and NIMALASURIYA, ANANDA. 1939. "Adaptation to a Low Calcium Intake in Reference to the Calcium Requirements of a Tropical Population," *J. Nutrition*, **18,** 563–77.

OLMSTED, J. M. D. 1938. *Claude Bernard, Physiologist.* New York: Harper & Bros.

OLSER, WILLIAM. 1932. *A Way of Life.* Baltimore: Remington-Putnam Book Co.

OSGOOD, EDWIN E., and BAKER, RUSSEL L. 1935. "Erythrocyte, Hemoglobin, Cell Volume and Color, Volume and Saturation Index Standards for Normal Children of School Age," *Amer. J. Dis. Child.*, **50,** 343–58.

OSSERMAN, ELLIOTT F., PITTS, GROVER C., WELHAM, WALTER C., and BEHNKE, A. R. 1950. "*In Vivo* Measurement of Body Fat and Body Water in a Group of Normal Men," *J. Appl. Physiol.*, **2,** 633–39.

PACE, NELLO, and RATHBUN, EDITH N. 1945. "Studies on Body Composition. III. The Body Water and Chemically Combined Nitrogen Content in Relation to Fat Content," *J. Biol. Chem.*, **158,** 685–91.

PACE, NELLO, KLINE, LEO, SCHACHMAN, HOWARD K., and HARFENIST, MORTON. 1947. "Studies on Body Composition. IV. Use of Radioactive Hydrogen for Measurement *in Vivo* of Total Body Water," *J. Biol. Chem.*, **168,** 459–69.

PALMER, WALTER W., MEANS, JAMES H., and GAMBLE, JAMES L. 1914. "Basal Metabolism and Creatinine Elimination," *J. Biol. Chem.*, **19,** 239–44.

POTTER, M. M. 1925. "Physical Manifestation of Fatigue in Young Children." Master's thesis, University of Chicago.

PRYOR, HELEN BRENTON. 1943. *As the Child Grows.* New York: Silver Burdett Co.

PRYOR, J. W. 1905. *Development of the Bones of the Hand as Shown by the X-Ray Method.* ("Bull. State Coll. Kentucky," Ser. 2, No. 5.) Lexington, Ky.

———. 1906. *Ossification of the Epiphyses of the Hand; X-Ray Method.* ("Bull. State Coll. Kentucky," Ser. 3, No. 4.) Lexington, Ky.

PRYOR, J. W. 1908. *The Chronology and Order of Ossification of the Bones of the Human Carpus.* ("Bull. State Univ. Kentucky," N.S., No. 2.) Lexington, Ky.

———. 1916. *Some Observations on the Ossification of the Bones of the Hand.* ("Bull. State Univ. Kentucky," Ser. 8, No. 11.) Lexington, Ky.

———. 1923. "Differences in the Time of Development of Centers of Ossification in the Male and Female Skeleton," *Anat. Record,* **25,** 257–73.

———. 1925. "Time of Ossification of Bones of the Hand of the Male and Female and Union of Epiphyses with the Diaphyses," *Amer. J. Phys. Anthrop.,* **8,** 401–10.

———. 1928. "Difference in the Ossification of the Male and Female Skeleton," *J. Anat.,* **62,** 499–506.

PYLE, S. IDELL, and HOERR, NORMAND L. 1955. *Radiographic Atlas of Skeletal Development of the Knee: A Standard of Reference.* Springfield, Ill.: Charles C Thomas.

PYLE, S. IDELL, MANN, ARVIN W., DREIZEN, SAMUEL, KELLY, HARRIET J., MACY, ICIE G., and SPIES, TOM D. 1948. "A Substitute for Skeletal Age (Todd) for Clinical Use: The Red Graph Method," *J. Pediat.,* **32,** 125–36.

Recommended Dietary Allowances. 1953. Rev. ed. Washington, D.C.: Food and Nutrition Board, National Research Council.

REDFIELD, JANET E., and MEREDITH, HOWARD V. 1938. "Changes in the Stature and Sitting Height of Pre-school Children in Relation to Rest in the Recumbent Position and Activity Following Rest," *Child Devel.,* **9,** 293–302.

REYNOLDS, EARLE L. 1944. "Differential Tissue Growth in the Leg during Childhood," *Child Devel.,* **15,** 181–205.

———. 1948. "Distribution of Tissue Components in the Female Leg from Birth to Maturity," *Anat. Record,* **100,** 621–30.

REYNOLDS, LAWRENCE, MACY, ICIE G., and SOUDERS, HELEN J. 1939. "The Gastrointestinal Response of Children to Test Meals of Barium and Pasteurized, Evaporated, and Base-exchanged Milks," *J. Pediat.,* **15,** 1–12.

ROSE, WILLIAM C. 1949. "Amino Acid Requirements of Man," *Federation Proc.,* **8,** 546–52.

ROTCH, THOMAS MORGAN. 1908. "Chronologic and Anatomic Age in Early Life," *J. Amer. Med. Assoc.,* **51,** 1197–1205.

———. 1909. "A Study of the Development of the Bones in Childhood by the Roentgen Method, with the View of Establishing a Developmental Index for the Grading of and the Protection of Early Life," *Trans. Assoc. Amer. Physicians,* **24,** 603–24.

———. 1910a. "A Comparison in Boys and Girls of Height, Weight and Epiphyseal Development," *Trans. Amer. Pediat. Soc.,* **22,** 36–38.

———. 1910b. "Roentgen Ray Methods Applied to the Grading of Early Life," *Amer. Phys. Educ. Rev.,* **15,** 396–420.

ROTCH, THOMAS MORGAN, and SMITH, HAROLD WELLINGTON. 1910. "A Study of the Development of the Epiphyses of the Hand and Wrist for the Purpose of Classifying the Cadets at Annapolis," *Trans. Assoc. Amer. Physicians,* **25,** 200–211.

SCAMMON, RICHARD E. 1923. "A Summary of the Anatomy of the Infant and Child," in *Abt's Pediatrics,* Vol. I. Philadelphia: W. B. Saunders Co.

———. 1927. "The First Seriation Study of Human Growth," *Amer. J. Phys. Anthrop.,* **10,** 329–36.

———. 1930. "The Measurement of the Body in Childhood," in HARRIS, J. A., JACKSON, C. M., PATERSON, D. G., and SCAMMON, R. E., *The Measurement of Man.* Minneapolis: University of Minnesota Press.

———. 1942. "Developmental Anatomy," in SCHAEFFER, J. PARSONS (ed.), *Human Anatomy: A Complete Systematic Treatise,* Sec. 1, pp. 9–52. 10th ed. Philadelphia: Blakiston Co.

SCHOENHEIMER, RUDOLF. 1942. *The Dynamic State of Body Constituents.* ("Harvard University Monographs in Medicine and Public Health.") Cambridge, Mass.: Harvard University Press.

SELYE, HANS. 1952. *The Story of the Adaptation Syndrome.* Montreal: Acta, Inc.

SHAFFER, PHILIP. 1908. "The Excretion of Kreatinin and Kreatin in Health and Disease," *Amer. J. Physiol.,* **23,** 1–22.

SHOHL, ALFRED T. 1939. *Mineral Metabolism.* New York: Reinhold Publishing Corp.

SIEGLING, JOHN A. 1941. "Growth of the Epiphyses," *J. Bone & Joint Surg.,* **23,** 23–36.

SIGERIST, HENRY E. 1933. *The Great Doctors: A Biographical History of Medicine.* Trans. EDEN and CEDAR PAUL. New York: W. W. Norton & Co.

SMUTS, D. B. 1935. "The Relation between the Basal Metabolism and the Endogenous Nitrogen Metabolism, with Particular Reference to the Estimation of the Maintenance Requirement of Protein," *J. Nutrition,* **9,** 403–33.

SOBERMAN, ROBERT J. 1949. "A Comparison of Total Body Water as Determined by Antipyrine and Desiccation in Rabbits," *Proc. Soc. Expt. Biol. Med.,* **71,** 172–73.

SOBERMAN, ROBERT, BRODIE, BERNARD B., LEVY, BETTY B., AXELROD, JULIUS, HOLLANDER, VINCENT, and STEELE, J. MURRAY. 1949. "The Use of Antipyrine in the Measurement of Total Body Water in Man," *J. Biol. Chem.,* **179,** 31–42.

SPRAY, CHRISTINE M., and WIDDOWSON, ELSIE M. 1950. "The Effect of Growth and Development on the Composition of Mammals," *Brit. J. Nutrition,* **4,** 332–53.

STEARNS, GENEVIEVE. 1931. "The Significance of the Retention Ratio of Calcium: Phosphorus in Infants and in Children," *Amer. J. Dis. Child.,* **42,** 749–59.

———. 1939. "The Mineral Metabolism of Normal Infants," *Physiol. Rev.,* **19,** 415–38.

———. 1951. In AMERICAN MEDICAL ASSOCIATION, *Handbook of Nutrition.* 2d ed. New York: Blakiston Co.

STEARNS, GENEVIEVE, and MOORE, DOROTHY L. R. 1931. "Growth in Height and Weight, and Retention of Nitrogen, Calcium and Phosphorus during Recovery from Severe Malnutrition," *Amer. J. Dis. Child.,* **42,** 774–80.

STEELE, J. MURRAY. 1950. "Body Water: An Editorial," *Amer. J. Med.,* **9,** 141–42.

STEELE, J. MURRAY, BERGER, E. Y., DUNNING, MARCELLE F., and BRODIE, BERNARD B. 1950. "Total Body Water in Man," *Amer. J. Physiol.,* **162,** 313–17.

STUART, HAROLD C., and DIVINELL, PENELOPE HILL. 1942. "The Growth of Bone, Muscle and Overlying Tissues in Children Six to Ten Years of Age as Revealed by Studies of Roentgenograms of the Leg Area," *Child Devel.,* **13,** 195–213.

STUART, HAROLD C., HILL, PENELOPE, and SHAW, CONSTANCE. 1940. *The Growth of Bone, Muscle and Overlying Tissues as Revealed by Studies of Roentgenograms of the Leg Area.* ("Society for Research in Child Development Monographs," Vol. V, No. 3.) Chicago.

STUART, HAROLD C., and MEREDITH, HOWARD V. 1946. "Use of Body Measurements in the School Health Program," *Amer. J. Public Health,* **36,** 1365–86.

TALBOT, FRITZ B. 1938. "Basal Metabolism Standards for Children," *Amer. J. Dis. Child.,* **55,** 455–59.

TALBOT, FRITZ B., WILSON, EDWIN B., and WORCESTER, JANE. 1937. "Basal Metabolism of Girls: Physiologic Background and Application of Standards," *Amer. J. Dis. Child.,* **53,** 273–347.

TALBOT, NATHAN B. 1936. "Basal Energy Metabolism and Creatinine in the Urine. I. Observations on Children," *Amer. J. Dis. Child.,* **52,** 16–24.

TANNER, J. M. 1947. "The Morphological Level of Personality," *Proc. Roy. Soc. Med.,* **40,** 301–8.

———. 1953. "Growth and Constitution," in KROEBER, A. L. (ed.), *Anthropology Today: An Encyclopedic Inventory,* pp. 750–70. Chicago: University of Chicago Press.

TODD, T. WINGATE. 1932. "Hereditary and Environmental Factors in Racial Development," *J. Orthodontia,* **18,** 799–811.

———. 1933. "The Developmental Health Examination," *J. Pediat.,* **3,** 415–23.

———. 1934. "An X-Ray Study of Nutritional Deviations," *J. Home Econ.,* **26,** 605–9.

———. 1935*a.* "Anthropology and Growth," *Science,* **81,** 259–63.

———. 1935*b.* "An Objective Study of Constitution in the Child," in *Proceedings of the Thomas P. Hinman Midwinter Clinic.* Reported in *Dental Cosmos,* **77,** 847–50.

———. 1937. *Atlas of Skeletal Maturation.* St. Louis: C. V. Mosby Co.

———. 1938. "The Record of Metabolism Imprinted on the Skeleton," *Amer. J. Orthodontics Oral Surg.,* **24,** 811–26.

VAN LIERE, EDWARD J., SLEETH, CLARK K., and NORTHRUP, DAVID. 1937. "The Relation of the Size of the Meal to the Emptying Time of the Human Stomach," *Amer. J. Physiol.,* **119,** 480–82.

VERZÁR, F., and McDOUGALL, E. J. 1936. *Absorption from the Intestine.* New York: Longmans, Green & Co.

WASHBURN, S. L. 1953. "The Strategy of Physical Anthropology," in KROEBER, A. L. (ed.), *Anthropology Today: An Encyclopedic Inventory,* pp. 714–27. Chicago: University of Chicago Press.

WEDGWOOD, RALPH J., BASS, DAVID E., KLIMAS, JULIE A., KLEEMAN, CHARLES R., and QUINN, MURRAY. 1953. "Relationship of Body Composition to Basal Metabolic Rate in Normal Man," *J. Appl. Physiol.,* **6,** 317–34.

WELHAM, W. C., and BEHNKE, ALBERT R. 1942. "The Specific Gravity of Healthy Men: Body Weight ÷ Volume and Other Physical Characteristics of Exceptional Athletes and of Naval Personnel," *J. Amer. Med. Assn.,* **118,** 498–501.

WETZEL, NORMAN C. 1943a. "Assessing the Physical Condition of Children. I. Case Demonstration of Failing Growth and the Determination of 'Par' by the Grid Method," *J. Pediat.,* **22,** 82–110.

———. 1943b. "Assessing the Physical Condition of Children. II. Simple Malnutrition: A Problem of Failing Growth and Development," *ibid.,* pp. 208–25.

———. 1943c. "Assessing the Physical Condition of Children. III. The Components of Physical Status and Physical Progress and Their Evaluation," *ibid.,* pp. 329–61.

———. 1944. "Growth," in *Medical Physics,* **1,** 513–69. Chicago: Year Book Publisher.

———. 1948. *The Treatment of Growth Failure of Children: An Application of the Grid Technic.* Cleveland: NEA Service, Inc.

WHITE HOUSE CONFERENCE ON CHILD HEALTH AND PROTECTION. 1932a. *Growth and Development of the Child,* Part III: *Nutrition.* New York: Century Co.

———. 1932b. *Growth and Development of the Child,* Part IV: *Appraisement of the Child.* New York: Century Co.

WIDDOWSON, E. M., McCANCE, R. A., and SPRAY, C. M. 1951. "The Chemical Composition of the Human Body," *Clin. Sci.,* **10,** 113–25.

WILLIAMS, HAROLD H., and ANDERSON, WILLIAM E. 1937. "The Relation of Lipids to Physiological Activity," *Oil and Soap,* **14,** 122–24.

WILLIAMS, HAROLD H., ERICKSON, BETTY N., and MACY, ICIE G. 1941. "Chemical Structure of the Red Blood Cell," *Quart. Rev. Biol.,* **16,** 80–89.

WILLIER, BENJAMIN H., WEISS, PAUL A., and HAMBURGER, VIKTOR (eds.). 1955. *Analysis of Development.* Philadelphia: W. B. Saunders Co.

WILMER, HARRY A., and SCAMMON, RICHARD E. 1945. "The Use of Iconometrography in Graphic Exposition. I. Topography and Composition of the Human Body," *Human Biol.,* **17,** 314–39.

ZOOK, DOTT EARL. 1932. "The Physical Growth of Boys: A Study by Means of Water Displacement," *Amer. J. Dis. Child.,* **43,** 1347–1432.

Index

Abdomen circumference, 30, 118
Absorption, nutrient, 59, 61
Activity, assessments, 16
  energy available for, 92
Adolph, E. F., 111
Age, of subjects, 30
Albritton, Evrett C., 43
Ammonia nitrogen, 103
Anatomic age; *see also* Skeletal assessments
  and body water, 72
  of subjects, 30
Anion balance, 95
Anthropometric measurements, 12, 28, 39, 85
  of subjects, 30, 32, 118
Ashworth, Ural S., 20, 86, 127

Baldwin, Bird T., 36, 111
Barcroft, Joseph, 110
Basal heat production, 20, 30, 85, 92
Bayer, Leona M., 27
Bayley, Nancy, 30
Beach, Eliot F., xi
Beck, Elizabeth I., 81
Behnke, Albert R., 4, 67, 68, 69, 70, 77, 79, 80, 110, 125
Benedict, F. G., 20
Berger, E. Y., 70, 77
Bernard, Claude, 28, 108, 109
Bert, M. H., 102
Biacromial width, 30
Biologic time, 6
Bitter, H. L., 70
Blood
  composition and growth, 113–17
  determinations, 22
Blyth, Carl S., 70, 78, 80
Body
  adaptation of, 118, 126
  composition of, 67, 69, 71, 81, 85, 100, 122, 127
  soft-hard tissue of, 100
  structure and function, 2
Body build, 3, 27
  assessment, 12, 29
Body type
  change in, 121
  indexes for determining, 32

Body water, 70
Bound, Louise E., 13
Boyd, Edith, 30, 70, 77, 111
Bricker, Mildred L., 104
Brodie, Bernard B., 70, 77
Brody, Samuel, 20, 86, 127
Brown, Walter N., Jr., 39
Brožek, Josef, 70, 75, 77
Busby, Laura M., 36, 111

Calcium
  absorption, 61, 62, 90, 99
  in blood serum, 115
  cations from, 96
  exchange, 105
  in feces, 54, 62
  intake, 46, 62
  retention, 37, 62–65, 90, 99
  in urine, 56, 62
Cannon, Walter B., 109
Carbohydrate
  absorbed, 61
  gastric response to, 47
  intake, 46
Carbohydrates, complex, in feces, 53
Carbon exchange, 105
Cassels, Donald E., 70, 74, 75, 76
Cation balance, 96
Cell mass, 69, 81
Cell solids, 69, 81
Cellulose, 25, 53
Chemical determinations, 16
Chemical maturity, 68
Chest measurements, 30, 32, 118
Children studied; *see* Subjects studied
Children's Fund of Michigan, vii, x
Children's Hospital of Michigan, ix, x
Chittenden, Russell, H., 1
Chlorine
  absorption, 61, 62
  anions from, 95
  in feces, 54, 62
  intake, 46, 62
  in red blood cells, 115
  retention, 62–65
  in urine, 56, 62
Chronologic age, 6, 30
  and body water, 72
Clark, Leland C., Jr., 81

145

Natural Institute of Health for the Study of Rheumatic Diseases, xi

Negative minerals
  absorption, 61, 62
  anions from, 95
  in feces, 54, 62
  intake, 46, 62
  retention, 62–65
  in urine, 57, 62

Nicholls, Lucius, 97

Nimalasuriya, Ananda, 97

Nitrogen
  absorption, 61, 90, 94, 99
  in blood, 115
  fecal, 102
  partition in urine, 85, 103
  in protein exchange, 93
  retention, 90, 94, 99
  in urine, 55

Nucleic acids, 100

Nutrients, assimilation of, 87

Nutritional conditioning, 17

Olson, Mary B., 25, 46

Osserman, Elliott F., 70, 77

Ossification, 14, 15

Oxygen consumption, 20, 79, 85, 106

Pace, Nello, 70, 77

Palmer, Lizzie Merrill, ix

Palmer, Walter W., 19

Pelidisi, the, 32, 34, 122

Phosphorus
  absorption, 61, 62, 90, 99
  anions from, 95
  in blood serum, 115
  in feces, 54, 62
  intake, 46, 62
  retention, 62–65, 90, 99
  in urine, 56, 62

Physical build; *see* Body build

Physiologic fuel value, 92

Physique assessment, 34

Pinneau, Samuel R., 30

Pirquet, Clemens von, 34

Pitts, Grover C., 70, 77

Ponderal index, 32

Positive minerals
  absorption, 61, 62
  cations from, 96
  in feces, 54, 62
  intake, 46, 62
  retention, 62–65
  in urine, 57, 62

Potassium
  absorption, 61, 62, 99
  in blood, 115
  cations from, 96
  in feces, 54, 62
  intake, 46, 62
  retention, 62–65, 99
  in urine, 56, 62

Potter, M. M., 13

Procter, Robert C., 20, 86, 127

Protein
  absorbed, 61
  content of body, 71
  energy and, 91
  exchange, 93
  intake, 46

Protoplasmic mass, 81

Pryor, Helen, 30, 34, 73

Pryor, J. W., 35, 36

Psychometric observations, 11

Pyle, S. Idell, 30, 37, 38, 118

Rathbun, Edith N., 77

Red blood cells, 114

Redfield, Janet E., 13

Research Laboratory, Children's Fund of Michigan, x

Reynolds, Earle L., 39

Reynolds, Lawrence, 24, 25, 46

Robinson, H. E., xi

Rotch, Thomas M., 36, 111

Ruttinger, Vera, xi

Scammon, Richard E., 13, 27, 30, 48, 49, 67, 86, 87, 127, 128

Schachman, Howard K., 70

Schloerb, Paul R., 73, 81

Schultz, Frederick W., 70, 74–76

Shaffer, Philip, 19

Shaw, Constance, 39

Sheldon, David B., 73, 81

Shohl, Alfred T., 52, 97

Shoulder, skeletal maturation of, 37

Shoulder width, 30, 118

Sigerist, Henry E., 108

Skeletal assessments, 14, 35
  of subjects, 37
  value of, 15, 39

Skin excretion, 57

Smith, Harold W., 36

Smith, Janice M., 104

Smith, Robert E., 77

Smuts, D. B., 104

Soberman, Robert J., 70